Editor
Jennifer Overend Prior, M. Ed.

Editorial Project Manager
Lori Kamola, M.S. Ed.

Editor-in-Chief
Sharon Coan, M.S. Ed.

Cover Artist
Lesley Palmer

Art Coordinator
Denice Adorno

Imaging
Alfred Lau
James Edward Grace
Temo Parra

Product Manager
Phil Garcia

Project Developer
Edward Fry, Ph.D.

Publishers
Rachelle Cracchiolo, M.S. Ed.
Mary Dupuy Smith, M.S. Ed.

NONFICTION COMPREHENSION
Test Practice

Author
Sarah K. Clark
Introduction by Kathleen Lewis, M.A.

Project Developer
Edward Fry, Ph.D.

Reading Passages provided by
TIME FOR KIDS magazine

Teacher Created Materials, Inc.
6421 Industry Way
Westminster, CA 92683
www.teachercreated.com
ISBN-0-7439-3511-X
©2001 Teacher Created Materials, Inc.
Reprinted, 2001
Made in U.S.A.

Table of Contents

(**Note:** Each six-part lesson revolves around an article from *Time For Kids*. The article titles are listed here for you to choose topics that will appeal to your students, but the individual articles do not begin on the first page of the lessons. The lessons in this book may be done in any order.)

Introduction

Why Every Teacher Needs This Book

In a day of increased accountability and standards-based instruction, teachers are feeling greater pressure for their students to perform well on standardized tests. Every teacher knows that students who can read, and comprehend what they read, will have better test performance.

In many classrooms today, teachers experience challenges they are not trained to meet, including limited English speakers, students with disabilities, high student mobility rates, and student apathy. Many states with poor standardized test scores have students that come from print-poor environments. Teachers need help developing competent readers and students who can apply their knowledge in the standardized test setting.

The *Nonfiction Comprehension Test Practice* series is a tool that will help teachers to teach comprehension skills to their students and enable their students to perform better in a test setting. This series supplies motivating, readable, interesting, nonfiction text, and comprehension exercises to help students practice comprehension skills while truly becoming better readers. The activities can be quick or in depth, allowing students to practice skills daily. What is practiced daily will be acquired by students. Practice for standardized tests needs to be started at the beginning of the school year, not a few weeks before the tests. The articles in this series are current and develop knowledge about today's world as well as the past. Students will begin thinking, talking, and developing a framework of knowledge which is crucial for comprehension.

When a teacher sparks an interest in knowledge, students will become life-long learners. In the process of completing these test practice activities, not only will you improve your students' test scores, you will create better readers and life-long learners.

Readability

All of the articles used in this series have been edited for readability. The Fry Graph, The Dale-Chall Readability Formula, or the Spache Readability Formula was used depending on the level of the article. Of more than 100 predictive readability formulas, these are the most widely used. These formulas count and factor in three variables: the number of words, syllables, and sentences. The Dale-Chall and Spache formulas also use vocabulary lists. The Dale-Chall Formula is typically used for upper-elementary and secondary grade-level materials. It uses its own vocabulary list and takes into account the total number of words and sentences. The formula reliably gives the readability for the chosen text. The Spache Formula is vocabulary-based, paying close attention to the percentage of words not present in the formula's vocabulary list. This formula is best for evaluating primary and early elementary texts. Through the use of these formulas, the levels of the articles are appropriate and comprehensible for students at each grade level.

Introduction (cont.)

General Lesson Plan

At each grade level of this series, there are 20 articles that prove interesting and readable to students. Each article is followed by questions on the following topics:

Sentence comprehension—Five true/false statements are related back to one sentence from the text.

Word study—One word from the text is explained (origin, part of speech, unique meaning, etc.). Activities can include completion items (cloze statements), making illustrations, or compare and contrast items.

Paragraph comprehension—This section contains one paragraph from the text and five multiple-choice questions directly related to that paragraph. The questions range from drawing information directly from the page to forming opinions and using outside knowledge.

Whole story comprehension—Eight multiple-choice questions relate back to the whole article or a major part of it. They can include comprehension that is factual, is based on opinion, involves inference, uses background knowledge, involves sequencing or classifying, relates to cause and effect, and involves understanding the author's intent. All levels of reading comprehension are covered.

Enrichment for language mechanics and expression—This section develops language mechanics and expression through a variety of activities.

Graphic development—Graphic organizers that relate to the article are used to answer a variety of comprehension questions. In some lessons, students create their own maps, graphs, and diagrams that relate to the article.

The following is a list of words from the lessons that may be difficult for some students. These words are listed here so that you may review them with your students as needed.

Word	Page	Word	Page	Word	Page
hyphen	19	Meriwether	45	allergic	73
Missouri	21	Ankylosaur	51	Egrets	81
eureka	27	paleontologist	51	Ibis	81
sauntered	29	Tyrannosaurus	51	phosphorus	81
onomatopoeia	31	Nodosaurid	51	ferocious	83
marathon	33	Cretaceous	51	Brontosaurus	87
simile	35	browser	59	rhetorical	95
embarrassed	39	graffiti	63	Pilanesberg	99
camaraderie	39	alliteration	65	Minke	137
quotations	41	denotation	71		

Introduction *(cont.)*

What Do Students Need to Learn?

Successful reading requires comprehension. Comprehending means having the ability to connect words and thoughts to knowledge already possessed. If you have little or no knowledge of a subject, it is difficult to comprehend an article or text written on that subject. Comprehension requires motivation and interest. Once your students start acquiring knowledge, they will want to fill in the gaps and learn more.

In order to help students be the best readers they can be, a teacher needs to be familiar with what students need to know to comprehend well. A teacher needs to know Bloom's levels of comprehension, traditional comprehension skills and expected products, and the types of questions that are generally used on standardized comprehension tests, as well as methods that can be used to help students to build a framework for comprehension.

Bloom's Taxonomy

In 1956, Benjamin Bloom created a classification for questions that are commonly used to demonstrate comprehension. These levels are listed here along with the corresponding skills that will demonstrate understanding and are important to remember when teaching comprehension to assure that students have attained higher levels of comprehension. Use this classification to form your own questions whenever students read or listen to literature.

Knowledge—Students will recall information. They will show knowledge of dates, events, places, and main ideas. Questions will include words such as: who, what, where, when, list, identify, and name.

Comprehension—Students will understand information. They will compare and contrast, order, categorize, and predict consequences. Questions will include words such as: compare, contrast, describe, summarize, predict, and estimate.

Application—Students will use information in new situations. Questions will include words such as: apply, demonstrate, solve, classify, and complete.

Analysis—Students will see patterns. They will be able to organize parts and figure out meaning. Questions will include words such as: order, explain, arrange, and analyze.

Synthesis—Students will use old ideas to create new ones. They will generalize, predict, and draw conclusions. Questions will include words such as: what if?, rewrite, rearrange, combine, create, and substitute.

Evaluation—Students will compare ideas and assess value. They will make choices and understand a subjective viewpoint. Questions will include words such as: assess, decide, and support your opinion.

Introduction *(cont.)*

Comprehension Skills

There are many skills that form the complex activity of comprehension. This wide range of understandings and abilities develops over time in competent readers. The following list includes many traditional skills found in scope and sequence charts and standards for reading comprehension.

identifies details

recognizes stated main idea

follows directions

determines sequence

recalls details

locates reference

recalls gist of story

labels parts

summarizes

recognizes anaphoric relationships

identifies time sequence

describes a character

retells story in own words

infers main idea

infers details

infers cause and effect

infers authors purpose/intent

classifies, places into categories

compares and contrasts

draws conclusions

makes generalizations

recognizes paragraph (text) organization

predicts outcome

recognizes hyperbole and exaggeration

experiences empathy for a character

experiences an emotional reaction to the text

judges quality/appeal of text

judges author's qualifications

recognizes facts vs. opinions

applies understanding to a new situation

recognizes literary style

recognizes figurative language

identifies mood

identifies plot and story line

Introduction (cont.)

Observable Comprehension Products

There are many exercises that students can complete when they comprehend the material they read. Some of these products can be performed orally in small groups. Some lend themselves more to independent paper-and-pencil type activities. Although there are more, the following are common and comprehensive products of comprehension.

Recognizing—underlining, multiple choice items, matching, true/false statements

Recalling—writing a short answer, filling in the blanks, flashcard question and answer

Paraphrasing—retelling in own words, summarizing

Classifying—grouping components, naming clusters, completing comparison tables, ordering components on a scale

Following directions—completing steps in a task, using a recipe, constructing

Visualizing—graphing, drawing a map, illustrating, making a time line, creating a flow chart

Fluent reading—accurate pronunciation, phrasing, intonation, dramatic qualities

Reading Comprehension Questions

Teaching the kinds of questions that appear on standardized tests gives students the framework to anticipate and thus look for the answers to questions while reading. This framework will not only help students' scores, but it will actually help them learn how to comprehend what they are reading. Some of the types of questions students will find on standardized comprehension tests are as follows:

Vocabulary—These questions are based on word meaning, common words, proper nouns, technical words, geographical words, and unusual adjectives.

Facts—These questions ask exactly what was written, using who, what, when, where, why, how, and how many.

Sequence—These questions are based on order—what happened first, last, and in between.

Conditionals—These questions use qualifying terms such as: if, could, alleged, etc.

Summarizing—These questions require students to restate, choose main ideas, conclude, and create a new title. Also important here is for students to understand and state the author's purpose.

Outcomes—These questions often involve readers drawing upon their own experiences or bringing outside knowledge to the composition. Students must understand cause and effect, results of actions, and implications.

Opinion—These questions ask the author's intent and mood and require use of background knowledge to answer.

Introduction (cont.)

Graphic Organizers

Reading and comprehension can be easier for students with a few simple practices. For top comprehension, students need a wide vocabulary, ideas about the subject they are reading, and understanding of the structure of the text. Pre-reading activities will help students in all of these areas. Graphic organizers help students build vocabulary, brainstorm ideas, and understand the structure of the text.

Graphic organizers aid students with vocabulary and comprehension. Graphic organizers can help students comprehend more and, in turn, gain insight into how to comprehend in future readings. This process teaches a student a way to connect new information to prior knowledge that is stored in his or her brain. Different types of graphic organizers are listed below by category.

Concept organizers include: semantic maps, spider maps (word webs), Venn diagrams, and fishbone diagrams.

Semantic map—This organizer builds vocabulary. A word for study is placed in the center of the page, and four categories are made around it. The categories expand on the nature of the word and relate it back to personal knowledge and experience of the students.

Spider map (word web)—The topic, concept, or theme is placed in the middle of the page. Like a spider's web, thoughts and ideas come out from the center, beginning with main ideas and flowing out to details.

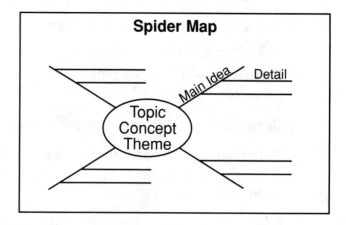

Introduction *(cont.)*

Venn diagram—This organizer compares and contrasts two ideas. With two large circles intersecting, each circle represents a different topic. The area of each circle that does not intersect is for ideas and concepts that are only true about one topic. The intersection is for ideas and concepts that are true about both topics.

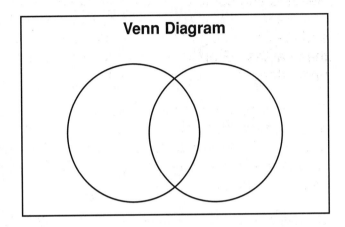

Fishbone diagram—This organizer deals with cause and effect. The result is listed first, branching out in a fishbone pattern with the causes that lead up to the result, along with other effects that happened along the way.

Continuum organizers can be linear or circular and contain a chain of events. These include time lines, chain of events, multiple linear maps, and circular or repeating maps.

Time lines—Whether graphing ancient history or the last hour, time lines help students to see how events have progressed and understand patterns in history.

Introduction (cont.)

Chain of Events—This organizer not only shows the progression of time but also emphasizes cause and effect. Beginning with the initiating event inside of a box, subsequent arrows and boxes follow showing the events in order.

Multiple linear maps—These organizers can help students visualize how different events can be happening at the same time, either in history or in a story, and how those events affect each other.

Circular or repeating maps—These organizers lend themselves to events that happen in a repeating pattern like events in science, such as the water cycle.

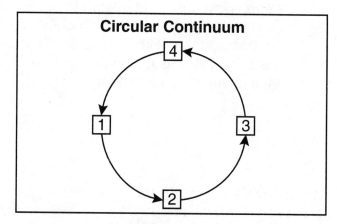

Hierarchical organizers show structure. These include: network trees, structured overviews, and class/example and properties maps. These organizers help students begin to visualize and comprehend hierarchy of knowledge, going from the big picture to the details.

Network tree—This organizer begins with a main, general topic. From there it branches out to examples of that topic, further branching out with more and more detail.

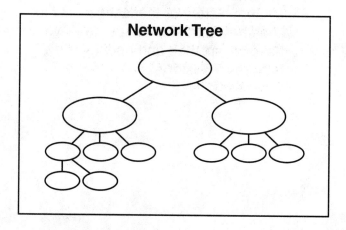

Introduction *(cont.)*

=== Graphic Organizers *(cont.)* ===

Structured overview—This is very similar to a network tree, but it varies in that it has a very structured look.

Class/example and properties map—Organized graphically, this map gives the information of class, example, and properties.

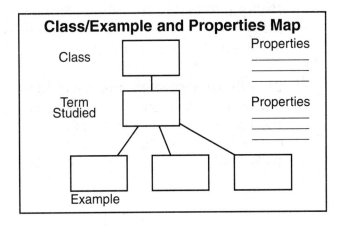

Spreadsheets are important organizers today. Much computer information is stored on spreadsheets. It is important for students to learn how to create, read, and comprehend these organizers. These include semantic feature analysis, compare and contrast matrices, and simple spreadsheet tables.

Semantic feature analysis—This organizer gives examples of a topic and lists features. A plus or a minus indicates if that example possesses those features.

===== Graphic Organizers *(cont.)* =====

Compare and contrast matrix—This organizer compares and contrasts two or more examples on different attributes.

Compare/Contrast Matrix (Spreadsheets)		
Attribute 1		
Attribute 2		
Attribute 3		

Simple spreadsheet table—Much information can be visualized through spreadsheets or tables. Choose examples and qualities and arrange them in spreadsheet style.

Maps are helpful in understanding spatial relationships. There are geographical maps, but there are also street maps and floor plans.

Geographical map—These organizers can range from globes to cities and details are limited.

Street map—Information on this type of organizer becomes more detailed.

Floor plan—This organizer becomes more detailed, from a building to a room or a student's desk.

Numerical graphs such as bar graphs, pie charts, and tables become important in comprehension, too.

Bar graph—With a vertical and a horizontal axis, this graph shows a comparison between subjects. It is important to be able to draw the correct information out of it.

Pie chart—In the circular shape of a pie, amounts totaling 100% are shown as pieces of pie. Once again, drawing correct information is important.

Using graphic organizers while reading class material will help students know what to do in order to better comprehend material on standardized comprehension tests. Further, a varied use of all types of organizers will help students of different learning styles hit a method that works for them.

===== Pre-reading Strategies =====

It is widely understood that for comprehension and acquisition to take place, new information must be integrated with what the reader knows. Pre-reading strategies will help students to build knowledge and restructure the information they already possess in order to more fully comprehend what they are reading. After a teacher has spent time teaching pre-reading strategies, students will know what to do when reading on their own.

Introduction *(cont.)*

Building Vocabulary

Common sense reveals that there is a symbiotic relationship between knowledge of vocabulary and comprehension. Vocabulary development and comprehension span the curriculum. Students come across a large and diverse vocabulary in science, social science, mathematics, art, and even physical education. Skills and strategies for understanding vocabulary can be taught throughout the day. You can build your students' vocabulary directly and/or indirectly. Both ways have shown merit for different learners, so a combination will be sure to help all of the learners in your classroom.

Whether done directly or indirectly, teaching the kind of vocabulary that occurs in a text will greatly improve comprehension. Teaching vocabulary directly, a teacher would list the vocabulary in the text and have the students find the definitions in some manner. Indirectly, a teacher would introduce the content of the text and then elicit vocabulary that the students bring with them on the subject. The use of graphic organizers is helpful in doing this. (See page 8 for different types.) The teacher would lead the discussion to specific words if necessary.

Direct teaching—The more conventional way of teaching vocabulary has its merits. Give students a list of vocabulary words and they look them up. This way teaches the use of reference materials and for some learners it is a good way to learn vocabulary. However, students truly learn vocabulary when they are involved in the construction of meaning rather than simply memorizing definitions.

Incidental or indirect teaching—This is really a combination of direct teaching and incidental learning for the well-equipped teacher. Teaching in this fashion, a teacher uses the students' knowledge and interests to begin a vocabulary development session that will end with what he or she wants the students to learn. Along the way, the teacher builds a grand vocabulary list and student interest. Also, students buy into the fact that they are part of the process and that learning vocabulary can be a personal experience that they can control. The students will learn how to become independent learners, studying things that interest them.

A general approach to building vocabulary could include the following:

Semantic association—Students brainstorm a list of words associated with a familiar word, sharing everyone's knowledge of vocabulary and discussing the less familiar words.

Semantic mapping—Once the brainstorming is done, students can group the words into categories, creating a visual organization to understand relationships.

Semantic feature analysis—Another way to group words is according to certain features. Use a chart to show similarities and differences between words.

Analogies—This practice will further help students to see the relationships of words. Also, analogies are often used on standardized tests. (e.g., Doctor is to patient as teacher is to _student_.)

Word roots and origins—The study of these, as well as affixes, will help students to deduce new words. Students can ask themselves, "Does it look like a word I know? Can I figure out the meaning in the given context?"

Building Vocabulary *(cont.)*

Synonyms and antonyms—The study of these related words provides a structure for meaning and is also good practice for learning and building vocabulary.

Brainstorming—The use of graphic organizers to list and categorize ideas will help greatly with comprehension. A great way to get started is with a KWL chart. By listing ideas that are known, what students want to know, and, when finished, what they learned, relationships will be established so that comprehension and acquisition of knowledge will take place. Word webs work well, too. Anticipating the types of words and ideas that will appear in the text will help with fluency of reading as well as with comprehension.

Understanding Structure

To be able to make predictions and find information in writing, a student must understand structure. From the structure of a sentence to a paragraph to an essay, this skill is important and sometimes overlooked in instruction. Some students have been so immersed in literature that they have a natural understanding of structure. For instance, they know that a fairy tale starts out "Once upon a time . . . ," has a good guy and a bad guy, has a problem with a solution, and ends ". . . happily ever after." But when a student does not have this prior knowledge, making heads or tails of a fairy tale is difficult. The same holds true with not understanding that the first sentence of a paragraph will probably contain the main idea, followed with examples of that idea. When looking back at a piece to find the answer to a question, understanding structure will allow students to quickly scan the text for the correct area in which to find the information. Furthermore, knowing where a text is going to go structurally will help prediction as well as comprehension.

Building a large vocabulary is important for comprehension, but comprehension and acquisition also require a framework for relating new information to what is already in the brain. Students must be taught the structure of sentences and paragraphs. Knowing the structure of these, they will begin to anticipate and predict what will come next. Not having to decode every word reduces the time spent reading a sentence and thus helps students remember what they read at the beginning of the sentence. Assessing an author's purpose and quickly recalling a graphic or framework of personal knowledge will help a reader predict and anticipate what vocabulary and ideas might come up in an article or story.

Several activities will help with understanding structure. The following list offers some ideas to help students:

Write—A great way to understand structure is to use it. Teach students the proper structure when they write.

Color code—When reading a text, students can use colored pencils or crayons to color code certain elements such as main idea, supporting sentences, and details. Once the colors are in place, they can study and tell in their own words about paragraph structure.

Introduction *(cont.)*

Go back in the text—Discuss a comprehension question with students. Ask them, "What kinds of words are you going to look for in the text to find the answer? Where are you going to look for them?" (The students should pick main ideas in the question and look for those words in the topic sentences of the different paragraphs.)

Graphic organizers—Use the list of graphic organizers (page 8) to find one that will suit your text. Have students create an organizer as a class, in a small group, or with a partner.

Study common order—Students can also look for common orders. Types of orders can include chronological, serial, logical, functional, spatial, and hierarchical.

━━━━━━ Standardized Tests ━━━━━━

Standardized tests have taken a great importance in education today. As an educator, you know that standardized tests do not necessarily provide an accurate picture of a student. There are many factors that do not reflect the students' competence that sway the results of these tests.

- The diversity of our big country makes the tests difficult to norm.
- Students that are talented in areas other than math and language cannot show this talent.
- Students who do not speak and read English fluently will not do well on standardized tests.
- Students who live in poverty do not necessarily have the experiences necessary to comprehend the questions.

The list could go on, but there does have to be some sort of assessment of progress that a community can use to decide how the schools are doing. Standardized tests and their results are receiving more and more attention these days. The purpose of this series, along with creating better readers, is to help students get better results on standardized tests.

━━━━━━ Test Success ━━━━━━

The ability to do well when taking traditional standardized tests on comprehension requires at least three things:

- a large vocabulary of sight words
- the mastery of certain specific test-taking skills
- the ability to recognize and control stress

Vocabulary has already been discussed in detail. Test-taking skills and recognizing and controlling stress can be taught and will be discussed in this section.

Introduction *(cont.)*

Every student in your class needs good test-taking skills, and almost all of them will need to be taught these skills. Even fluent readers and extremely logical students will fair better on standardized tests if they are taught a few simple skills for taking tests.

These test-taking skills are:

- The ability to follow complicated and sometimes confusing directions. Teach students to break down the directions and translate them into easy, understandable words. Use this series to teach them the types of questions that will appear.

- The ability to scale back what they know and concentrate on just what is asked and what is contained in the text—show them how to restrict their responses. Question students on their answers when doing practice exercises and have them show where they found the answer in the text.

- The ability to rule out confusing distracters in multiple choice answers. Teach students to look for key words and match up the information from the text.

- The ability to maintain concentration during boring and tedious repetition. Use practice time to practice this and reward students for maintaining concentration. Explain to students why they are practicing and why their concentration is important for the day of the test.

There are also environmental elements that you can practice with throughout the year in order for your students to become more accustomed to them for the testing period.

If your desks are pushed together, have students move them apart so they will be accustomed to the feel on test-taking day.

- Put a "Testing—Do Not Disturb" sign on the door.

- Require "test etiquette" when practicing: no talking, attentive listening, and following directions.

- Provide a strip of construction paper for each student to use as a marker.

- Establish a routine for replacing broken pencils. Give each student two sharpened pencils and have a back-up supply ready. Tell students they will need to raise their broken pencil in their hand, and you will give them a new one. One thing students should not worry about is the teacher's reaction to a broken pencil.

- Read the instructions to the students as you would when giving a standardized test so they grow accustomed to your test-giving voice.

- As a teacher, you probably realize that what is practiced daily is what is best learned. All of these practices work well to help students improve their scores.

Introduction *(cont.)*

Reduce Stress and Build Confidence

As well as the physical and mental aspects of test-taking, there is also the psychological. It is important to reduce students' stress and increase students' confidence during the year.

- In order to reduce stress, it first needs to be recognized. Discuss feelings and apprehensions about testing. Give students some tools for handling stress.

- Begin talking about good habits at the beginning of the year. Talk about getting enough sleep, eating a good breakfast, and exercising before and after school. Consider sending home a letter encouraging parents to start these good routines with their children at home.

- Explain the power of positive thought to your students. Tell them to use their imaginations to visualize themselves doing well. Let them know that they have practiced all year and are ready for what is to come.

- Remember to let students stretch and walk around between tests. Try using "Simon Says" with younger students throughout the year to get them to breathe deeply, stretch, and relax so it won't be a novel idea during test time.

- Build confidence during the year when using the practice tests. Emphasize that these tests are for learning. If they could get all of the answers right the first time, they wouldn't need any practice. Encourage students to state at least one thing they learned from doing the practice test.

- Give credit for reasonable answers. Explain to students that the test makers write answers that seem almost true to really test the students' understanding. Encourage students to explain why they chose the answers they gave, and then reason with the whole class on how not to be duped the next time.

- Promote a relaxed, positive outlook on test-taking. Let your students know on the real day that they are fully prepared to do their best.

Introduction *(cont.)*

Suggestions for the Teacher

When practicing skills for comprehension, it is important to vocalize and discuss the process in finding an answer. After building vocabulary, tapping background knowledge, and discussing the structure that might be used in the article, have the students read the article. If they are not able to read the article independently, have them read with a partner or in a small teacher-lead group. After completing these steps, work through the comprehension questions. The following are suggestions for working through these activities.

- Have students read the text silently and answer the questions.

- Have students correct their own papers.

- Discuss each answer and how the students came to their answers.

- Refer to the exact wording in the text.

- Discuss whether students had to tap their own knowledge or not.

Answer Sheet

The teacher can choose to use the blank answer sheet located at the back of the book for practice filling in bubble forms for standardized tests. The rows have not been numbered so that the teacher can use the form for any test, filling in the numbers and copying for the class as necessary. The teacher can also have the students write the answers directly on the pages of the test practice sheets instead of using the bubble sheet.

Summary

Teachers need to find a way to blend test preparation with the process of learning and discovery. It is important for students to learn test-taking skills and strategies because they will be important throughout life. It is more important for students to build vocabulary and knowledge, to create frameworks for comprehension, and to become fluent readers.

The *Nonfiction Comprehension Test Practice* series is an outstanding program to start your students in the direction of becoming better readers and test-takers. These are skills they will need throughout life. Provide an atmosphere of the joy of learning and create a climate for curiosity within your classroom. With daily practice of comprehension skills and test-taking procedures, teaching comprehension may seem just a little bit easier.

Whole Story Comprehension

Directions: Read the story below and answer the questions on the following page.

A New Dino Duo

As a paleontologist, James Kirkland has examined thousands of different dinosaur bones. But even he wasn't prepared for what he saw when he was called to investigate some new fossils found near Salt Lake City, Utah. A fossil bed there held the bones of two never-before-seen species of Ankylosaur. The discovery is changing scientists' ideas about the history of dinosaurs in America.

Both of the newly discovered creatures belong to a group of plant-eating dinosaurs called Ankylosaur, which means "fused lizards." The name comes from the heavy armor-like plates attached or fused to their heads. Some grew more than 30 feet long.

"These two dinosaurs were very similar animals in many respects," says Kirkland. One is an Ankylosaurid. An Ankylosaurid had big armored plates around the head and a long tail with a heavy club at the end. It would swing the club tail to fight bigger animals, like the Tyrannosaurus Rex.

The other new species, the Nodosaurid, was also well armed. "It had spikes on its shoulders that it used to ram larger creatures," says Kirkland. "These dinosaurs were built like tanks."

Most Ankylosaurs lived 148 million to 64 million years ago, during the last dinosaur era, known as the Late Cretaceous period. They lived in Asia and apparently crossed over to America on a land bridge that once connected Asia to what is now Alaska.

"Ankylosauria was in a real hurry to get over here from Asia," says Kirkland. "They were some of the first to get here."

By studying volcanic ash found near the site, scientists have determined that the Ankylosaurid bones were 25 million years older than any other known American Ankylosaur. This means that the land bridge must have existed earlier than scientists had believed. Paleontologist Kenneth Carpenter says these findings push the date that the land bridge existed back from 90 million years ago to 110 million years ago.

The skull and armor of the Ankylosaurid and the shoulder blade of the Nodosaurid are being studied by experts at the College of Eastern Utah Prehistoric Museum. Already they have learned that the head armor of the Ankylosaurid is not a bunch of plates attached to its head, but an outgrowth of its skull bones. They are eager to discover more about these armed warriors of a lost world.

Whole Story Comprehension *(cont.)*

Directions: After you have read the story on the previous page, answer the questions below.

1. Who is James Kirkland?

    a. a scientist who studies lizards

    b. a professor

    c. a paleontologist

    d. a doctor

2. The discovery of these fossils is changing scientists' ideas about what?

    a. the history of the land bridge

    b. the history of the earth

    c. the beginning of fossil fuels

    d. the history of dinosaurs

3. The word Ankylosaur means

    a. fused lizards.

    b. lizards with caps.

    c. lizards with extra legs.

    d. lizards with shells.

4. From what does the name "fused lizards" come?

    a. the spikes on the head

    b. the heavy armor-like plates

    c. the fusing of two lizards

    d. the legs of the lizard, fused together

5. The Ankylosaurids would fight bigger animals such as

    a. Stegosaurus.

    b. Bronchosaurus.

    c. Tyrannosaurus Rex.

    d. Achranid.

6. What did the scientists study to determine that the bones were 25 million years old?

    a. the armor-like plates

    b. the land bridge

    c. the dinosaur fossils

    d. volcanic ash

7. The land bridge must have existed _____ than scientists believed.

    a. later

    b. earlier

    c. in a larger scale

    d. closer to Asia

8. What have scientists learned about the head armor?

    a. They learned it broke off easily.

    b. They learned it was also found on the Tyrannosaurus Rex.

    c. They learned that the armor is not a bunch of plates attached to its head, but an outgrowth of skull bones.

    d. They learned it was cartilage instead of bones.

Enrichment

Directions: Read the following information and use it to match the words with the definitions below.

> James Kirkland is a scientist that studies dinosaur bones. He is called a *paleontologist*. A paleontologist studies a science called *paleontology*. There are many words that end in "ology." The suffix "ology" means "the science of" or "the study of" something. For example, *mineralogy* is the study of *minerals*. Many of these words are used when studying social studies and science.

Words

1. _____ meteorology

2. _____ biology

3. _____ cytology

4. _____ dermatology

5. _____ pomology

6. _____ genealogy

7. _____ entomology

8. _____ sociology

9. _____ toxicology

Definitions

A. Study of insects

B. Study of fruit

C. Study of poisons

D. Study of ancestors

E. Study of cells

F. Study of life

G. Study of weather

H. Study of skin

I. Study of society

Graphic Development

Directions: Dinosaurs lived millions of years ago. There are many different eras that date back millions of years. The dinosaurs were part of the Mesozoic Era. Use the chart below to answer the questions.

Dating Dinosaurs

(mya = million years ago)

Phanerozoic Eon (544 mya to present)	Cenozoic Era (65 mya to today)	Quaternary (1.8 mya to today)
		    Holocene (11,000 mya to today)
		    Plestocene (1.8 mya to 11,000 yrs.)
		Tertiary (65 to 1.8 mya)
		    Pliocene (5 to 1.8 mya)
		    Miocene (23 to 5 mya)
		    Oligocene (38 to 23 mya)
		    Eocene (54 to 38 mya)
		    Paleocene (65 to 54 mya)

	Mesozoic Era (245 to 65 mya)	Cretaceous (146 to 65 mya) Jurassic (208 to 146 mya) Triassic (245 to 208 mya)

	Paleozoic Era (544 to 245 mya)	Permian (286 to 245 mya)
		Carboniferous (360 to 286 mya)
		    Pennsylvanian (325 to 286 mya)
		    Mississippian (360 to 325 mya)
		Devonian (410 to 360 mya)
		Silurian (440 to 410 mya)
		Ordovician (505 to 440 mya)
		Cambrian (544 to 505 mya)
		    Tommotian (530 to 528 mya)

Precambrian Time (4,500 to 544 mya)	Proterozoic Era (2,500 to 544 mya)	Neoproterozoic (900 to 544 mya) Vendian (650 to 544 mya) Mesoproterozoic (1,600 to 900 mya) Paleoproterozoic (2,500 to 1,600 mya)
	Archaean (3,800 to 2,500 mya)	
	Hadean (450 to 3,800 mya)	

1. What is the title of the chart? _____

2. What do the letters mya stand for? _____

3. In what era were Cretaceous, Jurassic, and Triassic periods? _____

4. How many million years ago was the Proterozoic Era? _____

5. What era was 65 million years ago until today? _____

Sentence Comprehension

Directions: Read the following sentence carefully and answer the questions below "True" (T) or "False" (F).

In a chairlift ride, kids can pull their family and friends 30 feet up in the air, then let them free-fall back down.

1. The ride takes people up 40 feet in the air. _____

2. The people in the chairlift ride free-fall down. _____

3. Adults must operate the machines. _____

4. Shooting the family into space for 2 hours is a feature of the chairlift ride. _____

5. The chairlift ride is operated by the kids. _____

Word Study

Directions: Some words can be joined to form compound words. Put the words below together and write a brief meaning of the compound word.

toymaker

A toymaker designs and creates toys. Toymaker is also a compound word. A compound word is two separate words combined together to form a new word. The meaning of the new word usually has something to do with the separate words, but a compound word does take on a meaning of its own.

1. news + paper   compound word = _____

   meaning = _____

2. cow + boy   compound word = _____

   meaning = _____

3. hair + net   compound word = _____

   meaning = _____

4. home + bound   compound word = _____

   meaning = _____

Paragraph Comprehension

Directions: Read the paragraph below and answer the following questions.

Watching LEGOs being made is just one of the attractions at LEGOLAND California, a new theme park in Carlsbad, California. LEGOLAND has rides and shows, but what makes it special is its amazing LEGO constructions.

---

1. Where is LEGOLAND located in California?

   a. San Diego, CA

   b. Los Angeles, CA

   c. Newport Beach, CA

   d. Carlsbad, CA

2. What makes LEGOLAND special?

   a. The fact that it is a theme park.

   b. The fact that it is now open to the public.

   c. There are amazing LEGO constructions.

   d. The fact that kids are welcome at this theme park.

3. What could you expect to do at LEGOLAND?

   a. You can expect to see the largest whales there.

   b. You can expect to meet the president of the LEGO company.

   c. You can expect to meet famous characters there.

   d. You can expect to go on rides, see shows, and see amazing LEGO constructions.

4. What do you think a theme park is?

   a. a place where kids are welcome

   b. a park with activities and shows connected to a theme

   c. a park that is built in a large city, usually in California

   d. a park that has themes and toys to play with

5. What is made at LEGOLAND?

   a. LEGOs

   b. legs

   c. action figures

   d. LEGO containers

Whole Story Comprehension

Directions: Read the story below and answer the questions on the following page.

LEGOLAND

The machine cranks up and 450 degrees of fiery heat turns bright plastic to mush. Then the machine applies 150 tons of pressure to the plastic. Ten seconds later, out comes a LEGO, one of those molded-plastic building blocks you can combine to build almost anything, from a spaceship to a dragon.

Watching LEGOs being made is just one of the attractions at LEGOLAND California, a new theme park in Carlsbad, California. LEGOLAND has rides and shows, but what makes it special is its amazing LEGO constructions.

Master LEGO builders used 2 million blocks to create a 34-foot-long red dinosaur that towers above LEGOLAND Lake. More than 1 million blocks form the giant face of Albert Einstein in the park's Imagination Zone. More than 20 million were used to create incredibly detailed mini-versions of such great American cities as New Orleans, Washington, D.C., and New York City!

The California park is the first LEGOLAND park in the U.S. The original LEGOLAND opened in 1968 in Denmark. Danish toymaker Ole Kirk Christiansen invented the bright bricks 50 years ago. Since then, more than 189 billion have been made. That's almost 30 LEGO pieces for every person on the planet.

Nearly all of the 40 attractions at LEGOLAND California look like giant LEGOS. The rides don't move unless the kids make them work. Where else can you drive a LEGO boat or an electric LEGO car and get your own LEGO license? In a chairlift ride, kids can pull their family and friends 30 feet up in the air, then let them free-fall back down.

"Most parks are for everybody," says LEGOLAND spokeswoman Jonna Rae Barteges. "This whole park is just for kids."

Whole Story Comprehension (cont.)

Directions: After you have read the story on the previous page, answer the questions below.

1. What type of machine is being described in the first paragraph?

   a. one of the rides at LEGOLAND

   b. a giant face of Albert Einstein

   c. one of the constructions at LEGOLAND

   d. a LEGO-making machine

2. What types of things would you find on a brochure advertising LEGOLAND?

   a. the rides, shows, and LEGOLAND constructions

   b. the boat rides, the dinosaurs, and the kid-operated machines

   c. the newly built theme park in Denmark

   d. the inventor of LEGOs

3. Which cities have mini-versions made of them using LEGOs at LEGOLAND?

   a. New York City and Washington, D.C.

   b. New Orleans, New York City, and Washington, D.C.

   c. New Hampshire, New York, and New Orleans

   d. Chicago, New Orleans, and New York City

4. Who created the 34-foot-long dinosaur?

   a. scientists that make LEGOs

   b. children from nearby cities

   c. master LEGO builders

   d. kids that won a contest

5. Where and when was the first LEGOLAND built?

   a. Los Angeles, CA, in 1978

   b. Phoenix, AZ, in 1968

   c. Sweden in 2000

   d. Denmark in 1968

6. How many pieces of LEGOs have been made?

   a. 189 billion

   b. 150 billion

   c. 200 billion

   d. too many to count

7. For whom is LEGOLAND targeted?

   a. girls between 5–10

   b. boys between 5–10

   c. kids

   d. none of the above

8. How many years ago were LEGOs invented?

   a. a century ago

   b. a half of a century ago

   c. a quarter of a century ago

   d. none of the above

Enrichment

Directions: Read the information below and use it to answer the following questions.

Where in the World is LEGOLAND?

Years ago, when people heard the term LEGOLAND, they would have wondered where it was and who lived in that land. Now all kids know that LEGOLAND is a place of fun and adventure, filled with LEGOs. As new products and new items are invented, new terms and new uses of old words have been adopted into the English language.

Look at these examples of "new" words, just as a result of technology:

Browser: This is a tool or program that allows you to search the Web. The most common Web browsers used today are *Netscape Navigator* and *Internet Explorer*.

Chat Room: People from all over can "chat" with others online on a variety of subjects. You need to be careful about using chat rooms. Dangerous people sometimes get involved with chat rooms.

Cyberspace: This is another word for the Internet.

Download: This is transferring information or files from the Internet to your computer. You must be careful when downloading. This is how computer viruses are spread.

FAQ: This is the abbreviation for "frequently asked questions." There is usually a category under the help section for these questions on Web sites.

Online: This is when you are using the Internet. You are then online.

Search Engine: Search engines are helpful when researching topics.

Surfing: This is what you are doing when you are looking around on the Internet.

URL: A URL is the address of a Web site. You must be very specific and type the exact letters of an address. You cannot add spaces or letters that don't appear in the address.

Write the word from each sentence that is the "new" word or new use of an old word.

1. _____   The CD has a scratch in it.

2. _____   How many megabytes does your computer have?

3. _____   What is the URL for that Web site?

4. _____   They built a tower using LEGOs.

5. _____   The movie was a DVD, not a video.

Graphic Development

Directions: The new LEGOLAND theme park is now open and running. It is located in Carlsbad, California. But just where is Carlsbad? Look closely at the map and answer the questions below.

1. What gulf is Carlsbad, CA, next to?

   _____

2. Is LEGOLAND north or south of Sea World in San Diego, CA?

   _____

3. Is Carlsbad, CA, one of California's large or small cities?

   _____

4. If a person lived in Los Angeles, which direction would he or she be heading to get to LEGOLAND?

   _____

5. What interstate runs through Carlsbad, CA?

   _____

Sentence Comprehension

Directions: Read the following sentence carefully and answer the questions below "True" (T) or "False" (F).

> Writer Laurie Stroblas began the District Lines Poetry Project in 1994, hoping to give bus riders something better to stare at than ads or graffiti.

1. Laurie Stroblas is a student in Washington, D.C. _____
2. The poetry would replace ads and graffiti. _____
3. The District Lines Poetry Project began in 1994. _____
4. The project was to give bus riders something inspiring to read. _____
5. The project was intended to curb violence in the subways. _____

Word Study

Directions: Match the correct definition with the italicized homograph in each sentence.

> **board**
>
> Board is a word that has two definitions. *Board* can mean a piece of sawed lumber, but in this article it means to come up against or alongside, as in boarding the subway. These two words are called homographs. Homographs are words that are spelled the same but have different meanings and origins.

a. boil—bubbling of hot liquid   e. arms—body parts
b. boil—red swelling on the skin   f. arms—weapons
c. bark—tree covering   g. bank—land along a river
d. bark—sound a dog makes   h. bank—place of financial business

_____ 1. The *bank* was slippery and covered with moss.

_____ 2. His *bark* grew louder and louder as the darkness came.

_____ 3. The *boil* on her arm was painful and sore.

_____ 4. Greg is planning to use his *arms* to support the weight of the box.

_____ 5. Please take this check and deposit it at the *bank*.

_____ 6. You can stop stirring once it begins to *boil*.

Paragraph Comprehension

Directions: Read the paragraph below and answer the following questions.

"The response was incredible," says Stroblas. Last year, she decided to transfer her idea to the buses and picked new poems with the advice of 150 students. Organizations donated enough money to keep Metro Muse in subway stations all winter. In spring, a new crop of poems sprouted on city buses.

---

1. How did Stroblas get the money she needed to post the poems?

    a. She held fund raisers to earn the money.

    b. She gathered donations from willing parents.

    c. Organizations donated the money.

    d. The local PTA donated and raised money for the project.

2. What number of students contributed poems?

    a. 1,500 students

    b. 150 students

    c. all the middle school students

    d. 12 students

3. What was the response to the project like?

    a. not enough interest and so it was canceled

    b. mediocre, not much interest

    c. incredible

    d. none of the above

4. How were the poems selected?

    a. with the advice of students

    b. by a drawing

    c. The community voted.

    d. none of the above

5. When did a new crop of poems show up on city buses?

    a. next year

    b. in the spring

    c. next month

    d. when enough money has been raised to fund the project

Whole Story Comprehension

Directions: Read the story below and answer the questions on the following page.

The Poetry Express

Jazzy new signs in subway stations have been catching the eyes of commuters in Washington. Instead of rushing to board a train, people pause to read poems written by kids.

The lighted posters, called Metro Muse, are at 10 train stops in the busy city. On display: 12 thoughtful compositions to celebrate kids' creativity and to promote reading.

Writer Laurie Stroblas began the District Lines Poetry Project in 1994, hoping to give bus riders something better to stare at than ads or graffiti. She had been leading poetry workshops in public schools, so she asked her students to lend a hand.

"The response was incredible," says Stroblas. Last year, she decided to transfer her ideas to the buses and picked new poems with the advice of 150 students. Organizations donated enough money to keep Metro Muse in subway stations all winter. In spring, a new crop of poems sprouted on city buses.

What are the poems about? Snow falling, the arrival of a new year, love, fear, and peace. Cindy Rosales, a sixth grader at Oyster Elementary School, was inspired two years ago by her favorite type of music: "Kindness is the jazz," she wrote. "Bring the big jazz in. The big, whole jazz."

Like most poets, the kids had mixed feelings about letting the public read their private thoughts. "I would feel glad that someone read my poem," one girl said. "But I would feel sad if they missed their train."

Whole Story Comprehension (cont.)

Directions: After you have read the story on the previous page, answer the questions below.

1. Where are the poems posted?

    a. subway stations and trains

    b. subway stations and soon-to-be buses

    c. on the school grounds

    d. in the classroom

2. What is the occupation of Laurie Stroblas?

    a. a doctor

    b. a teacher

    c. a politician

    d. a writer and a teacher

3. What are some of the topics of the poems?

    a. death, hatred, and war

    b. love, fear, and peace

    c. school, tests, and fighting

    d. hope, fear, and rain

4. The District Lines Poetry Project was

    a. started in 1995.

    b. initiated by Laurie Stroblas.

    c. ordered to begin by the President.

    d. first for the parents and now for the kids.

5. What is the purpose of the Poetry Project?

    a. It promotes reading and spotlights children's creativity.

    b. It keeps children out of gangs.

    c. It supports the school's after school programs.

    d. It is the first of its kind to include the writings of teachers.

6. Select a new title that best fits the information in this article.

    a. The Poetry Pizza

    b. Kids First – Poetry Second

    c. Here Comes the Bus!

    d. The Metro Muse

7. Students have received inspiration for the poetry from

    a. ideas brainstormed as a class.

    b. other poems posted in the subway.

    c. music, personal thoughts, and experiences.

    d. poetry books.

8. How do the students feel about letting others read their poems?

    a. There are mixed feelings.

    b. All the kids are excited.

    c. The kids don't want the public to read their poems.

    d. None of the above

Enrichment

Directions: Read the information below and use it to answer the following questions.

Poetry is music to the ears. Poetry also provides a means to express thoughts, feelings, and ideas. The Metro Muse posters at 10 train stops in Washington are proof of the inspiration and positive feelings that poetry offers.

Language has rhythm and poetry taps into that rhythm. Consider the poem by sixth-grader Cindy Rosales, from "The Poetry Express":

> "Kindess is the jazz.
>
> Bring the big jazz in.
>
> The big,
>
> Whole jazz."

The words do not rhyme, as is often thought of with poetry, and yet, the words come to life and bring a rhyme of their own. Another type of rhythm with words is *alliteration*. Alliteration is the repetition of the beginning sound of two or more words in a sentence. Alliteration is often used with descriptions. Read the following examples of alliteration:

- A sleek, shiny red car slid into the driveway.
- A bold and brassy young lady bounced into the room.
- The cute, cuddly kitten came to where I sat.
- A bright and beautiful sun was beaming down this morning.

Circle the number beside each sentence that uses alliteration.

1. A brilliantly-beautiful baby bird sat up on the branch.

2. A red and green sailboat came into view.

3. The peaceful poem inspired hope and promise.

4. The song was a loud and noisy one.

5. A busy bumble bee buzzed boldly toward us.

Graphic Development

Directions: The poetry of children don the walls of subways and train stops in Washington to give riders something different to look at other than advertisements or graffiti. In metropolitan areas, signs are plentiful. Signs use symbols to carry the message to others. Interpret the symbols on the signs below.

1.

2.

3.

4.

5.

Sentence Comprehension

Directions: Read the following sentence carefully and answer the questions below "True" (T) or "False" (F).

In 1998, 181 million video and computer games were sold in the U.S.

---

1. In 1998, there were many computer and video games sold. _____

2. Only video games are allowed to be sold in the U.S. _____

3. Computer games are considered illegal. _____

4. Video games and computer games could be considered popular. _____

5. Not very many video and computer games were sold in 1998. _____

Word Study

Directions: Locate all the proper nouns in the second paragraph below and write them on the lines using capital letters.

Missouri

Missouri is one of fifty states in the United States of America. Missouri is a proper noun. A proper noun is different than a common noun. A proper noun is the name of a specific person, place, or thing. Proper nouns are always capitalized.

---

sandy was able to come visit us in november. It was cool outside and we were excited to jump in the leaves again. She always comes to visit us and grandma nan this time of year. It just wouldn't seem like thanksgiving without her. We really enjoy having her and her dog heidi come to see us.

1. _____

2. _____

3. _____

4. _____

5. _____

6. _____

Paragraph Comprehension

Directions: Read the paragraph below and answer the following questions.

> Surprisingly, experts who study kids and video games say games are not all bad. Some games build problem-solving skills. Unfortunately, kids can go overboard.

1. Unfortunately, what do kids do with video games?

    a. They can't figure out how to play the video games.

    b. They play them so much, the video games break.

    c. They go overboard and play them too much.

    d. They don't have enough time to play the video games.

2. Experts say that

    a. every family should have at least one video game.

    b. not all video games are bad.

    c. children aren't old enough to be playing video games.

    d. parents should be playing the video games with their children.

3. Video and computer games can be positive when

    a. they build problem-solving skills.

    b. they contain the basic nutrients and vitamins.

    c. they build self-esteem.

    d. they teach kids how to play fairly.

4. Experts have studied kids

    a. in Europe.

    b. and their parents.

    c. and computers.

    d. and video games.

5. Going overboard means

    a. jumping off the couch in the middle of a video game.

    b. eating all of your meals and playing video games at the same time.

    c. doing your homework before you play a video game.

    d. watching and playing video games too much of the time.

Whole Story Comprehension

Directions: Read the story below and answer the questions on the following page.

Hooked!

It's 10 A.M. on a Saturday. Ricky Picone, 11, and his brother David, 10, are soaked in sweat. Two seconds remain in the game, and David is up by one point. Ricky grabs the ball. He shoots; he scores! "Game over. You lose!" shouts Ricky.

A morning basketball game? Sort of. Except Ricky and David are in their basement and still in pajamas. They are playing video basketball. Their parents have been calling them to come up for breakfast for 25 minutes. Mom and Dad are not too happy.

Sound familiar? No wonder. Video games are big in kids' lives, and in some cases they've taken over!

In 1998, 181 million video and computer games were sold in the U.S. That's almost two games for every household. With all the cool new games, some kids can't stop playing.

You know the kids. The ones who spend more time with video games than eating or sleeping. "There's this one kid," says John Szendiuch, 12, of Pelham, New York. "They're his whole life."

When kids play all the time, parents get upset. Ron Hughes of Missouri found that he couldn't even talk to his son Russell, 9, when he was playing a video game. "The phone would ring," says Hughes, "and Russell wouldn't hear it."

Parents also worry about violence. The blood-gushing from many video games is enough to make some parents ban all video games. Surprisingly, experts who study kids and video games say games are not all bad. Some games build problem-solving skills. Unfortunately, kids can go overboard.

How do kids and parents keep playing under control? "It's important for parents to take an interest in what kids are playing," says expert David Walsh. "Then parents can make fair rules and understand why kids love the games."

Walsh believes parents must limit kids' playing time. He recommends no more than 90 minutes a day. But watch out! Kids are going to want to play even more. Video games are going to get bigger, brighter, and even harder for kids to resist.

Whole Story Comprehension *(cont.)*

Directions: After you have read the story on the previous page, answer the questions below.

1. The parents in this article feel
   a. happy and excited.
   b. excited and frustrated.
   c. confused and angry.
   d. frustrated and unhappy.

2. What has taken over the lives of some kids?
   a. the video games they play
   b. the television set
   c. the amount of homework they are required to do
   d. none of the above answers

3. Parents are concerned about the _____ in some video games.
   a. nudity
   b. violence
   c. language
   d. songs

4. What is the occupation of David Walsh?
   a. He makes video games.
   b. He is a scientific expert.
   c. He is a teacher.
   d. He is a concerned parent.

5. What does David Walsh recommend to parents?
   a. destroying all video games
   b. teaching children how to budget the money they spend on video games
   c. to take an interest in what kids are playing and setting limits
   d. buying more video games so that each child has a turn to play

6. Why do you think kids have a hard time playing the video games for short periods of time?
   a. The kids don't like to watch TV.
   b. The kids get hooked into a game and can't stop.
   c. The kids want to disobey their parents.
   d. The kids are trying to set the record for the amount of time they play the video games.

7. What do you think are some of the down sides of becoming so involved in playing the video and computer games?
   a. It's hard to take turns.
   b. There isn't enough time to play all the video games the kids have.
   c. The kids spend all of their time playing video games instead of talking with family and having a normal life.
   d. none of the above

8. What is the recommended amount of minutes suggested by experts?
   a. 100 minutes
   b. no more than 90 minutes
   c. no more than 50 minutes
   d. no more than 20 minutes

Enrichment

Directions: Read the information below and use it to answer the following questions.

It is obvious from the article on kids playing video and computer games that there is concern about the effects and the time spent playing these games. Parents often have a difficult time setting limits and getting the correct message sent to their kids. Sometimes parents say one thing, but kids interpret it to mean a different thing. This is where many of the parent/child conflicts happen. It's all in the interpretation of what we are saying.

In writing, there are two different kinds of meanings of the words you use. The **denotation** of a word is the meaning that you would find in the dictionary. The **connotation** of a word is the feeling or mental picture that people associate with the word.

For example, the words *notorious* and *famous* have different connotations. Notorious has a negative connotation. It makes you think that a person is well-known for bad or outrageous things. Famous suggests that a person is well known for all the good and wonderful things he or she did.

Here are some examples of connotations used in the article, "Hooked!" that you just read. The italicized words are taken from the article.

Negative words	**Positive Words**
grabs	takes
addicted	*hooked*
violence	aggression
mad	*upset*

Label each of the words below. Write positive or negative to describe its connotation.

1. _____ instantly/hastily _____

2. _____ debate/quarrel _____

3. _____ odor/fragrance _____

4. _____ snoop/investigate _____

5. _____ attract/lure _____

6. _____ call/yell _____

Graphic Development

Directions: Read the following information and then use the double line graph below to answer the questions.

More and more young people are playing video and computer games. Some say the habit is addictive. In 1998 alone, 181 million video and computer games were sold in the United States.

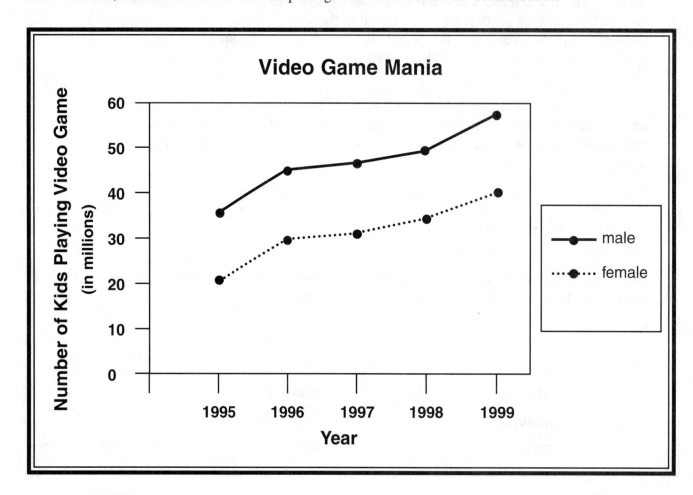

1. What does this graph show?

   _____

2. What number of boys played video games in 1997?

   _____

3. What is the title of this graph?

   _____

4. How many more boys than girls played video games in 1995?

   _____

5. How many more boys played video games in 1999 compared to 1995?

   _____

Sentence Comprehension

Directions: Read the following sentence carefully and answer the questions below "True" (T) or "False" (F).

People who are allergic to peanuts must avoid anything containing a peanut or its oil.

---

1. People can be allergic to peanuts. _____

2. People must avoid anything containing almond oil. _____

3. If people are allergic to peanuts, they should also avoid peanut oil. _____

4. All people are allergic to peanut oil. _____

5. An allergy to peanuts means you can't eat things with peanuts. _____

Word Study

Directions: Find six words below that have three syllables like the word sacrifice. Write these three-syllable words on the lines that follow.

Sacrifice
Sacrifice means to give up something for the sake of something else. Sacrifice is a word that has three syllables. A syllable is a unit of spoken language. In the dictionary, syllables are denoted with a dot or a hyphen between each syllable. Syllables aid in the pronunciation of a word.

---

amazing	curious	seaport	agriculture	nutritious
doubtful	science	together	interesting	misspelled
projects	height	mothering	bring	sandwiches

1. _____

2. _____

3. _____

4. _____

5. _____

6. _____

Paragraph Comprehension

Directions: Read the paragraph below and answer the following questions.

Banning peanut butter creates some sticky problems. Peanut-butter-and-jelly sandwiches are popular. They are nutritious, affordable food for most families. However, there are many choices for a healthful lunch. School cafeterias can provide a wide choice of foods that are safe for all kids. They can even send home suggestions for bag lunches that don't include peanuts. People should be willing to sacrifice a particular food if it might save a child's life. All schools should ban peanuts and peanut products.

1. Which type of sandwich is considered popular, but deadly to some kids?

   a. ham sandwiches

   b. sardine sandwiches

   c. jelly and cheese sandwiches

   d. peanut-butter-and-jelly sandwiches

2. Who could provide healthy and safe alternatives?

   a. the cafeterias

   b. the teachers

   c. the students that are allergic to peanuts

   d. the parents of the students

3. The author is ultimately trying to persuade schools to what?

   a. keep kids from getting allergies

   b. ban peanuts and peanut products from school

   c. build more playground equipment for students with allergies

   d. address the needs of all students with allergies

4. According to the article, who should ban peanuts and peanut products?

   a. the local grocery stores

   b. the schools

   c. the parent/teacher organizations

   d. the local school boards

5. Sacrificing peanut butter and peanuts could save what?

   a. time

   b. money

   c. a child's life

   d. none of the above

Whole Story Comprehension

Directions: Read the story below and answer the questions on the following page.

Peanut Problems

Some kids are allergic to peanuts. Should schools be nut-free zones? When Nicholas Pave was three years old, he ate a piece of brownie at a party. Within seconds, his throat was itching and his nose was running. An hour later, he started throwing up. Says Nicholas, now 7: "It was scary."

How can one bite of one brownie make someone so sick? Nicholas was having an allergic reaction to peanut butter chips in the brownie. His mom quickly called the doctor and gave Nicholas some medicine. Without the medicine, he might have stopped breathing. Some people allergic to peanuts have died after eating them.

People who are allergic to peanuts must avoid anything containing a peanut or its oil. Sometimes just smelling or touching peanut oil or peanut dust causes an allergic reaction. That can turn a school cafeteria into a danger zone!

Now some schools have decided not to take any chances. They're cracking down on peanut products to protect allergic kids. In some school cafeterias, peanut-free tables are being set aside. In other schools, no one is allowed to bring any "peanutty" foods at all.

Banning peanut butter creates some sticky problems. Peanut-butter-and-jelly sandwiches are popular. They are a nutritious, affordable food for most families. However, there are many choices for a healthful lunch. School cafeterias can provide a wide choice of foods that are safe for all kids. They can even send home suggestions for bag lunches that don't include peanuts. People should be willing to sacrifice a particular food if it might save a child's life. All schools should ban peanuts and peanut products.

Even if all schools don't ban peanuts, Ann Munoz-Furlong of the Food Allergy Network, points out that teachers and students should have an emergency plan to deal with any allergy attack. Allergic kids should always wash their hands before eating and should never trade foods with other kids. Kids should feel safe in the classroom and the cafeteria.

Whole Story Comprehension *(cont.)*

Directions: After you have read the story on the previous page, answer the questions below.

1. What symptoms did Nicholas have that indicated he had an allergy?

    a. His hands were sweaty.

    b. He began running a fever.

    c. He had an itchy throat and hives.

    d. He had itchy throat, runny nose, and began throwing up.

2. Without medicine, what could have happened to Nicholas?

    a. He could have eaten too many peanuts.

    b. He could have thrown up his food.

    c. He could have stopped breathing or even died.

    d. He could have eaten more brownies.

3. In some schools, students are not allowed to bring what types of foods?

    a. "peanutty" foods

    b. foods that have walnuts

    c. video games

    d. popcorn and peanuts

4. Other than just peanuts, what else can cause an allergic reaction?

    a. smelling or touching peanut oil or peanut dust

    b. dust mites

    c. peanuts and walnuts

    d. none of the above

5. What are some schools doing as a result of peanut allergies?

    a. sending home suggestions for students with allergies

    b. enlisting volunteers to watch for allergic students

    c. banning "peanutty" products

    d. serving a choice of brownies with peanuts or without peanuts

6. Which of the following statements is an opinion?

    a. People can be allergic to peanuts.

    b. Schools should ban all peanut products.

    c. Peanut-butter-and-jelly sandwiches are nutritious.

    d. People allergic to peanuts should avoid peanut oil as well.

7. The Food Allergy Network suggests that teachers should be prepared with

    a. an emergency plan in case someone has an allergic reaction.

    b. plenty of peanut butter.

    c. a list of suggestions for different types of sandwiches.

    d. information to give parents about allergies.

8. What tips should students with peanut allergies remember?

    a. Eat all of your lunch.

    b. Drink milk with sandwiches.

    c. Share food with only people you know.

    d. Wash hands before eating and never trade food.

Enrichment

Directions: Read the information below and use it to answer the following questions.

In the article about peanuts, there were many signal words. What are signal words? Signal words are used to connect ideas together. There are many types of signal words, and you probably already use them in your writing without knowing it. Look at the types of signal words below. The italicized words came from the article.

For example:

because	but	despite	*however*
so that	similar to	too	next
resulting from	later	lately	until
within	once	also	*though*
inside	*now*	and finally	*even*
so	although	more	

Signal words are used to help us understand what we read. Signal words help us understand how the information is organized and to provide clues about what is important. They help us anticipate the direction of a piece of writing. They tell us that there are more ideas to come, that there is an order to ideas, and that there is going to be a change of direction. They may also tell us where and when something is happening or give something emphasis. They prepare us for examples and tell us that a condition or modification is coming up. Signal words are independent of the content; they can be used with any piece of writing.

Select the correct signal word from the box to fill in the sentences. Some of the signal words may be used more than once, or not at all.

1. Some children are allergic to peanuts, _____ though they don't know it.

2. _____ of the danger to students, some schools are banning peanut products.

3. _____ the cafeteria has agreed to send home ideas for sack lunches, some parents are still very unhappy!

4. Scientists have _____ found that peanut oil and dust should also be avoided.

5. _____, schools should have an emergency plan for allergy attacks.

Graphic Development

Directions: Read the following information and then use the fictitious picture graph below to answer the questions about kids with allergies.

One in 20 kids has a food allergy. There are many food allergies, but there are other types of allergies as well. Some of these nonfood allergies include dust, pollen, lotions, and perfumes. An allergy is when the "body thinks that it is a harmful invader and tries to attack it."

Kids with Allergies at Hualapai Elementary School

Milk allergy	☺ ☺ ☺ ☺ ☺ ☺ ☺
Shell fish allergy	☺ ☺ ☺ ☺
Pollen allergy	☺ ☺
Nut allergy	☺ ☺ ☺ ☺ ☺
Wheat or soy allergy	☺ ☺ ☺

☺ = 5 students

1. What allergy do the most people in this graph have?

_____

2. How many more people have an allergy to nuts compared to people with an allergy to shellfish?

_____

3. What is the title of this graph?

_____

4. Which type of allergy on this chart has nothing to do with what a person eats?

_____

5. How many people are allergic to milk?

_____

Sentence Comprehension

Directions: Read the following sentence carefully and answer the questions below "True" (T) or "False" (F).

When large numbers of people began settling in Florida nearly a hundred years ago, the Everglades were considered a worthless swampland.

---

1. The large number of people settling in Florida helped to sustain the swampland. _____

2. The Everglades were thought to be worthless swampland. _____

3. Over a hundred years ago, people came and settled in the Everglades. _____

4. The Everglades are located in Oklahoma. _____

5. The Everglades didn't exist 100 years ago. _____

Word Study

Directions: Look below at the chart showing the meaning of the different word parts. Find the meaning of each word by combining the meanings of its parts from the chart.

Ecosystem is a word that is a combination of two words. The first part *eco-* means *habitat* or *environment*. *System* means *interdependent group of items forming a unified whole*. Combining the two parts makes the word *ecosystem* which means *the complex of a community and its environment functioning as an ecological unit in nature.*

Word	Prefix	Word Root	Suffix
dismissal	dis- "apart"	-mis- "to send"	-al "action"
complicate	com- "together"	-plic- "fold"	-ate "to make"
emotion	e- "out"	-mot- "to move"	-ion "state"
incredible	in- "not"	-cred- "to believe"	-ible "capable"
composer	com- "together"	-pos- "to place"	-er "a doer"
duplexity	du- "two"	-plex- "fold"	-ity "condition"
resonance	re-"again"	-son- "to sound"	-ance "condition"

1. commotion _____

2. mission _____

3. composer _____

4. emotional _____

5. expose _____

6. resonance _____

Paragraph Comprehension

Directions: Read the paragraph below and answer the following questions.

But a closer look reveals a busy, buzzing natural world. Hundreds of species make up the Everglades' ecosystem. Egrets and white Ibis soar above the water. Lime-green tree frogs croak. Craggy alligators lurk below the swamp's surface.

---

1. The Everglades contain hundreds of

    a. birds.

    b. frogs.

    c. species.

    d. alligators.

2. What are Egrets and white Ibis?

    a. reindeer

    b. extinct animals

    c. birds

    d. insects

3. The word craggy probably means

    a. rough and rugged.

    b. kind and considerate.

    c. patient and loving.

    d. calm and peaceful.

4. What lurks below the swamp?

    a. eel

    b. sharks

    c. crocodiles

    d. alligators

5. What color are the tree frogs?

    a. chartreuse

    b. lime-green

    c. dark green

    d. light green

Whole Story Comprehension

Directions: Read the story below and answer the questions on the following page.

Looking Out for the Gators

Florida's Everglades National Park doesn't look like much from an airplane. A flat, soggy field of tall grass stretches toward the horizon. A few trees dot the landscape under the hot Florida sun.

But a closer look reveals a busy, buzzing natural world. Hundreds of species make up the Everglades' ecosystem. Egrets and white Ibis soar above the water. Lime-green tree frogs croak. Craggy alligators lurk below the swamp's surface. Now, after years of bad planning, this habitat may be dying. Dozens of its species are endangered.

When large numbers of people began settling in Florida nearly a hundred years ago, the Everglades were considered a worthless swampland. Builders did their best to drain the swamp. Farms and cities sprang up where alligators once roamed freely.

In the 1920s, Army engineers straightened rivers and built canals and dikes to prevent flooding and keep water supplies stable for farms and cities. They didn't realize that changing the flow of water would harm the ecosystem drastically. The Everglades, which once covered 4,000 square miles, shrank by half. Populations of birds, alligators, and other animals shrank, too.

"Everything depends on the water," explains Sandy Dayhoff, education coordinator for Everglades National Park, "not only having enough water, but the right amount at the right time." Dayhoff compares the Everglades with a giant bathtub. In the rainy season, the tub is full. In the dry season, it slowly drains. Human activities are interfering with both parts of this natural cycle.

Farmers, especially sugar-cane growers, have created another problem. A chemical called phosphorus is found in crop fertilizers and animal wastes. Sugar-cane plantations and dairy farms dump tons of phosphorus into South Florida's waters every year.

Some plants absorb it better than others. Cattails, for example, are great at absorbing phosphorus. This plant is beginning to take over the park, crowding out native saw grass, which many animals need.

In the 1980s, people began to realize the Everglades were in trouble. Engineers are now trying to put rivers back on their old winding courses. It won't be cheap. The plan will cost $1.5 billion over seven years. Some say sugar-cane growers must pay their fair share. One idea is to add a tax on sugar that would help pay for the plan. But sugar growers say a tax would hurt their business and risk the jobs of 40,000 sugar workers.

Still, nearly everyone agrees that the Everglades must be rescued. "There's no other place like this on earth," says Dayhoff. "It would be terrible to destroy a national treasure like this."

Whole Story Comprehension *(cont.)*

Directions: After you have read the story on the previous page, answer the questions below.

1. What happened in the 1920s?

    a. Army engineers straightened rivers and built canals to prevent flooding.

    b. Hundreds and thousands of animals immediately became extinct.

    c. The swamp was closed down.

    d. Builders began requesting permits to reinstate animals on the endangered species list.

2. To what does Sandy Dayhoff compare the Everglades?

    a. a large lake

    b. the Atlantic Ocean

    c. a bathtub

    d. swamps in South America

3. What change affected the ecosystem?

    a. the amount of species in the Everglades

    b. the flow of water in the Everglades

    c. the amount of homes being built in the Everglades

    d. the number of animals located in the Everglades

4. The Everglades once covered how many square miles?

    a. 3,000

    b. 7,000

    c. 6,000

    d. 4,000

5. What type of growers have created another problem?

    a. sugar-cane growers

    b. wheat growers

    c. cotton growers

    d. orange growers

6. What problem does the chemical phosphorus cause?

    a. It causes all the plants to die.

    b. Cattails absorb this chemical faster than other plants, and they are starting to take over.

    c. The chemical gets in the food we eat.

    d. The chemical is leaving the land barren and so more crops can't be grown.

7. When did people begin to realize the Everglades were in trouble?

    a. 1920s

    b. 1960s

    c. 1970s

    d. 1980s

8. What is the plan that has been suggested to correct the problem?

    a. to take all the endangered animals out and transfer them to parks in the area

    b. to create new crops to take the place of the sugar crops

    c. to recreate the Everglades ecosystem somewhere else

    d. to put the rivers back on their old winding courses

Enrichment

Directions: Read the following information and use it to complete the sentences below.

"A flat, soggy field of tall grass stretches toward the horizon."

" . . . a closer look reveals a busy, buzzing natural world."

"A few trees dot the landscape under the hot Florida sun."

The author of "Looking Out for the Gators," selected colorful words to help paint the picture of the Everglades in Florida's National Park. Descriptive language usually comes from adjectives and adverbs. Adjectives describe nouns and adverbs describe verbs. Adverbs and adjectives can be powerful descriptive words in your writing, if used correctly. Look at how the adjectives and adverbs create more descriptive sentences below.

1. The *healthy, adorable* baby cooed *happily* into her mother's ear.

2. The *excited* couple *quickly* jumped into their limousine.

3. The *screaming* and *shouting* fans *hastily* lunged at the *famous* singer.

Practice using adverbs and adjectives by rewriting the sentences below. Select adjectives and adverbs from the word box to add more detail to the sentences.

List of Adverbs	List of Adjectives
happily	ferocious
angrily	magnificent
hastily	grand
sadly	craggy
lovingly	beautiful

1. The alligator swam.

   _____

2. The hundreds of species were dying.

   _____

3. The white Ibis flew.

   _____

4. Builders tore up the landscape.

   _____

5. The scientist was sad at the result of the chemicals.

   _____

Graphic Development

Directions: Read the following information and then use the fictional time line below to answer the questions.

The Everglades National Park is one of a kind. There is no other place like it on the earth. People have learned the damage that chemicals and years of bad planning have done to this fragile ecosystem. What will the years ahead hold in store for the Everglades?

Trouble in the Everglades

2000	Animals in the Everglades are on the endangered list.
1980s	People begin to realize the Everglades are in trouble.
1960s	Farmers begin using phosphorus, which affects the Everglades.
1940s	Building continues in the Everglades.
1920s	Army engineers straighten rivers and build canals.
1900s	Large numbers of people begin settling in Florida.

1. What did army engineers do in the 1920s?

   _____

2. In what decade did people begin to realize that the Everglades were in trouble?

   _____

3. What is the title of this time line?

   _____

4. What happened in the 1900s to the Everglades?

   _____

5. What is the name of the chemical being used in the 60s and 70s?

   _____

Sentence Comprehension

Directions: Read the following sentence carefully and answer the questions below "True" (T) or "False" (F).

Once a Beanie is no longer in stores, its value can skyrocket.

---

1. A Beanie can change in price. _____
2. The price of a Beanie increases when it's not in stores. _____
3. *Skyrocket* means the price goes up. _____
4. When Beanies are no longer available, they become worthless. _____
5. Beanies are always kept in stores. _____

Word Study

Directions: Match the words in Column A with their synonyms in Column B. The first one has been done for you.

---

urgent

The meaning of urgent is *calling for immediate attention*. A word that has a similar meaning to urgent is the word pressing. Synonyms are words that have similar meanings. Synonyms are used in dictionaries to define words.

Column A	Column B
1. add	make, construct
2. ask	under, below
3. bad	join, unite, combine
4. beneath	bring, lug, transport
5. bold	summon, command
6. brilliant	naughty, evil, wicked
7. call	bright, radiant
8. build	youngsters, kids
9. carry	question, inquire
10. children	valiant, brave, daring

Paragraph Comprehension

Directions: Read the paragraph below and answer the following questions.

The Beanie Baby boom began in 1996. The low price (about $5 apiece) and variety made them a huge hit. But what made them an even bigger hit was Ty's policy of "retiring" some Beanies every year. Once a Beanie is no longer in stores, its value can skyrocket. A rare Beanie, such as Bronty the Brontosaurus, was selling for as much as $1,300 last May. Lately, though, Beanie prices have fallen. Poor Bronty sold for $900 in August. However, prices rose again after the September announcement.

---

1. The cost of a Beanie Baby is about

    a. $4

    b. $5

    c. $3

    d. $1

2. Ty's policy does what each year?

    a. distributes 50 Beanies to needy children

    b. designs two new Beanies every year

    c. retires some Beanies every year

    d. solicits suggestions and ideas for new Beanies

3. Why do Beanies rise in price?

    a. Their availability becomes scarce.

    b. The Ty company begins charging less per Beanie.

    c. The kids no longer have coupons.

    d. The Beanies begin to drop in value.

4. What features of the Beanies made them a huge hit?

    a. the colors selected for the Beanies

    b. the low price and the variety

    c. the low supply of Beanies

    d. the announcement to retire all Beanies

5. What caused the prices to rise again in September?

    a. the holiday season coming up

    b. the value of toys dropped

    c. the crash of the stock market

    d. the announcement

Whole Story Comprehension

Directions: Read the story below and answer the questions on the following page.

Bye-Bye, Beanies?

December 31, 1999, was the end of the millennium. Would it be the end of Beanie Babies, too? In September, 1999, Ty, Inc., the maker of Beanie Babies, posted this urgent message on its Web site: "Very Important Notice: On December 31, 1999 . . . all Beanies will be retired."

The news came as a shock to Beanie fans of all ages. Stores selling Beanies saw a rush of buyers. "People know they're going to be worth more now," says New York City shopkeeper Joe Diamond.

That may be exactly what Ty, Inc. had in mind. Many Beanie collectors suspect that the announcement was a trick to renew interest in Beanies and to make them more valuable.

The Beanie Baby boom began in 1996. The low price (about $5 apiece) and variety made them a huge hit. But what made them an even bigger hit was Ty's policy of "retiring" some Beanies every year. Once a Beanie is no longer in stores, its value can skyrocket. A rare Beanie, such as Bronty the Brontosaurus, was selling for as much as $1,300 last May. Lately, though, Beanie prices have fallen. Poor Bronty sold for $900 in August. However, prices rose again after the September announcement.

Is Ty Inc. really getting out of the Beanie business? Mary Beth Sobolewski, editor of *Mary Beth's Bean Bag World Monthly* magazine, thinks the Ty company is full of beans. "I believe there will be an announcement of all new Beanies come January 1," she says.

Whole Story Comprehension *(cont.)*

Directions: After you have read the story on the previous page answer the questions below.

1. What did the announcement in December, 1999, say?

    a. a new line of Beanies would be introduced

    b. all the Beanies would be retired

    c. the price of Beanies would be going up

    d. the supply of Beanies would be greater than last year

2. What do Beanie collectors suspect about the announcement?

    a. that it was a mistake

    b. that it was a good sales tactic

    c. that it should affect Beanie collectors

    d. that it was a trick to renew interest in Beanies

3. Which of the following statements is a fact?

    a. Beanies are fun to collect.

    b. Beanies should be collected by kids only.

    c. Beanies are sure to decrease in value.

    d. The Beanie Baby boom began in 1996.

4. What is the name of Mary Beth's magazine?

    a. *Bean Bag World*

    b. *Beanies Make It Big*

    c. *Mary Beth's Bean Bag World Monthly*

    d. *Beanies Bonanza*

5. What is the occupation of Joe Diamond?

    a. editor

    b. Beanie collector

    c. CEO of Ty Beanie Babies

    d. shopkeeper

6. A new title for this article could be

    a. A New Twist.

    b. Bankin' on Beanie.

    c. A Fond Beanie Farewell?

    d. What's Up?

7. One of the rare Beanies is

    a. Frigid the Penguin.

    b. Bronty the Brontosaurus.

    c. Bonnie the Duck.

    d. Beanie the Baby.

8. What did people suspect would happen in January, 2000?

    a. all Beanies to be retired

    b. the Ty Co. to go out of business

    c. an announcement of all new Beanies

    d. a buy-one, get-one free

Enrichment

Directions: Read the information below and use it to find the plural from of the words that follow.

Spelling errors commonly occur when the writer changes a singular noun to a plural noun. Most plural words have an *s* added to them to become plural. There are many words where the spelling of the word changes by making it plural. Look at the following plural rules:

- Add an *s* to most nouns to make them plural.

- Nouns ending with a consonant and a *y* change the *y* to *i* and add *es*.

- Nouns that end in *ch, sh, ss, s, x, o, or s* add *es*. If the word ends in *f* or *fe*, you would usually change to *v* and then add *es*.

- Some words do not add endings, but change their form altogether. (For example: man—men, ox—oxen)

- Some words keep the same spelling in the plural form.

What is the plural form of each of these words? Some of these words are taken directly from the Beanie Baby article.

1. sale _____

2. suspect _____

3. address _____

4. Beanie _____

5. bean _____

6. potato _____

7. leaf _____

8. deer _____

9. worry _____

10. bunch _____

11. tooth _____

12. collector _____

13. mess _____

14. company _____

15. inch _____

16. coach _____

17. belief _____

18. thief _____

Graphic Development

Directions: Read the following information and use the line graph to answer the questions below.

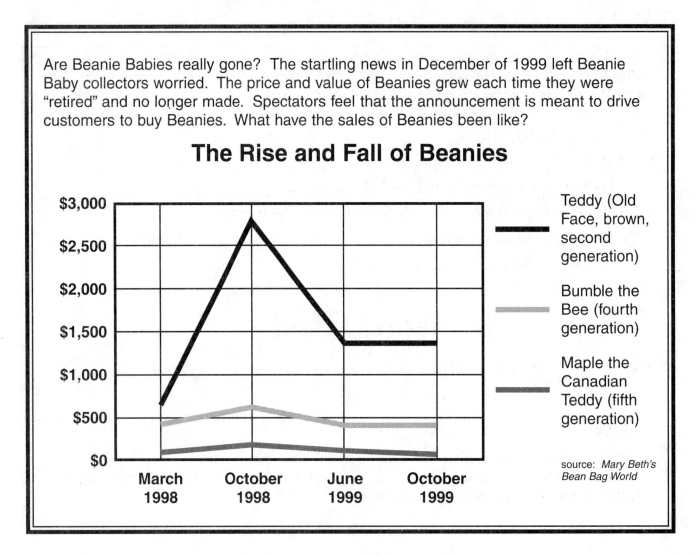

Are Beanie Babies really gone? The startling news in December of 1999 left Beanie Baby collectors worried. The price and value of Beanies grew each time they were "retired" and no longer made. Spectators feel that the announcement is meant to drive customers to buy Beanies. What have the sales of Beanies been like?

The Rise and Fall of Beanies

Teddy (Old Face, brown, second generation)

Bumble the Bee (fourth generation)

Maple the Canadian Teddy (fifth generation)

source: *Mary Beth's Bean Bag World*

1. In what year was the most amount of money spent on Beanies?

_____

2. Of the three Beanies displayed on this graph, which Beanie is purchased the most?

_____

3. What is the source of information for this graph?

_____

4. What is the title of this graph?

_____

5. How much more did Teddy cost than Bumble the Bee in October, 1999?

_____

Sentence Comprehension

Directions: Read the following sentence carefully and answer the questions below "True" (T) or "False" (F).

> Checketts, who calls himself a "high-thrill junkie," climbed to the very top of the 300-foot Power Tower soon after it was built.

1. Checketts is a high-thrill junkie. _____
2. Checketts was injured when he fell 300 feet. _____
3. Checketts climbed to the top of Power Tower before it was finished. _____
4. Checketts probably likes adventure. _____
5. This sentence is about all the amusement park rides in Las Vegas, Nevada. _____

Word Study

Directions: Select one of the suffixes from the box to add to one of the words below.

> **sickness**
>
> Sickness is an illness or a weakened condition. The suffix in sickness is *ness*. A suffix comes at the end of a word. A suffix can tell you what type of word it is part of and how it should be used in a sentence.

en (made of, make)	**ness** (with)	**ate** (cause, make)
al (relating to)	**able, ible** (able, can do)	**ship** (quality, skill)

1. nature + _____ = _____
2. weak + _____ = _____
3. friend + _____ = _____
4. careless + _____ = _____
5. agree + _____ = _____

Paragraph Comprehension

Directions: Read the paragraph below and answer the following questions.

"My job is a blast, literally," says Stan Checketts of Logan, Utah. Checketts gets paid to give people thrills and chills! He invents amusement park rides. "It's great for people to scream and smile and have a great rush," says Checketts, president of S&S Sports Power, Inc. His scream machine, Power Tower, at Cedar Point Amusement Park in Sandusky, Ohio, is the world's tallest tower ride. Riders shoot 240 feet up two of the ride's towers at the same time while the other riders drop down the other two towers. A strong blast of air pushes them all along at 50 miles an hour. The rides takes just three seconds each way.

---

1. Checketts gets paid to

   a. climb his amusement rides.

   b. warn people of amusement ride dangers.

   c. give people thrills and chills on amusement park rides.

   d. invent new amusement video games.

2. The name of Checketts' scream machine at Cedar Point is

   a. Tower of Terror.

   b. Power Plus.

   c. Cedar Point Terror.

   d. Power Tower.

3. The Power Tower is

   a. the first tower ever built.

   b. over its budget.

   c. the smallest tower ride in the world.

   d. the world's tallest tower ride.

4. What shoots people up at 50 mph?

   a. air

   b. water

   c. energy

   d. electricity

5. The ride takes only

   a. passengers that are four feet and under.

   b. three seconds each way.

   c. children.

   d. tickets.

Whole Story Comprehension

Directions: Read the story below and answer the questions on the following page.

Tower of Thrills

"My job is a blast, literally," says Stan Checketts of Logan, Utah. Checketts gets paid to give people thrills and chills! He invents amusement park rides. "It's great for people to scream and smile and have a great rush," says Checketts, president of S&S Sports Power, Inc. His scream machine, Power Tower, at Cedar Point Amusement Park in Sandusky, Ohio, is the world's tallest tower ride. Riders shoot 240 feet up two of the ride's towers at the same time while other riders drop down the other two towers. A strong blast of air pushes them along at 50 miles an hour. The ride takes just three seconds each way.

Checketts, who calls himself a "high-thrill junkie," climbed to the very top of the 300-foot Power Tower soon after it was built! He climbs all of his tallest creations. He even hiked up Big Shot, the tower ride he built on top of the fifth tallest building in the U.S., the Stratosphere Hotel in Las Vegas, Nevada.

Playing with kids inspired Checketts to build thrill rides like the Power Tower. "The concept evolved from tossing my nine children in the air when they were little," Checketts said. Now his eight grandchildren can get a high-speed rush on his rides. What do they think of his job? "They think Grandpa's crazy," laughs Checketts, who also bungee jumps, skydives, and climbs mountains.

There is one thing the brave Checketts can't stomach. Longer thrill rides, including many roller coasters, give him motion sickness! "Usually nobody gets sick on my rides," he says, "because they happen so quickly."

What will Checketts do now that he has built a record-breaking thrill ride? "There are still a lot of crazy ideas in my head for high-thrill rides," he says. Next: an air-powered roller coaster. Sounds like a blast!

Whole Story Comprehension (cont.)

Directions: After you have read the story on the previous page, answer the questions below.

1. A "high-thrill" junkie is someone who

    a. eats too much junk food.

    b. likes to do adventurous things.

    c. is addicted to drugs.

    d. is afraid of amusement parks.

2. What does Checketts do on all of his tall creations?

    a. climbs them

    b. jumps off of them

    c. enjoys taking pictures of them

    d. advertises them

3. What is the inspiration behind these tower rides?

    a. when Checketts rode on an airplane

    b. Checketts saw them in a movie

    c. the thrill of riding

    d. when Checketts used to toss his children in the air

4. Checketts' grandchildren think he is

    a. strong.

    b. brave.

    c. crazy.

    d. fun.

5. Which statement is an opinion?

    a. Checkett invents amusement park rides.

    b. Roller coasters give Checketts motion sickness.

    c. Checketts is a brave and exciting person.

    d. Checketts plans to build an air-powered roller coaster.

6. What other interests does Checketts have?

    a. bungee jumping, roller blading, and repelling

    b. bungee jumping, skydiving, and mountain climbing

    c. cooking, repelling, and mountain climbing

    d. mountain climbing and repelling

7. Checketts is President of

    a. Amusements, Inc.

    b. S&S Sports Power, Inc.

    c. Sports and Power, Inc.

    d. S&S Power Towers, Inc.

8. Where did Checketts build the ride Big Shot?

    a. In Chicago at the World Fair

    b. In New York City

    c. Atop the Stratosphere Hotel in Las Vegas

    d. On the fifth tallest building in Laughlin, Nevada

Enrichment

Directions: Read the information below and use it to answer the following questions.

The way you begin your writing will either leave the reader engaged or disinterested. There are many ways to capture the attention of the reader. Listed below are descriptions of leads that can be used to begin a piece of writing.

1. **Personal Experience**—Using personal experience gives the reader a chance to know you a little bit better. People can often relate to a personal experience and it helps connect with what you are writing about.

2. **Strong Visual Image**—Painting a picture for the reader captures their interest and helps them visualize what you are talking about. Visual images can create a lasting impression.

3. **Rhetorical Question**—A rhetorical question is a question you ask at the beginning to get the reader thinking. You never expect the reader to answer the question.

4. **Facts and Statistics**—Using facts and statistics can be a powerful tool, especially if the facts and statistics are amazing or disturbing. Facts and statistics can set the record straight from the beginning and can help establish validity for the topic being read.

5. **Dialogue/Quotation**—Using dialogue or a quote will entice the reader. Quotes and dialogues allow the reader to see what other people think about the subject. This gives you a chance to support your claims.

Place a number next to each sentence corresponding to the type of lead that has been used in the following beginnings. The first one has been done for you. The first one is also the same lead used in the actual article, "Tower of Thrills."

_____5_____ "My job is a blast, literally." says Stan Checketts of Logan, Utah. Checketts gets paid to give people thrills and chills! He invents amusement park rides.

_____ I remember the first time I ever rode on the Power Tower with my mother. The look of desperation and panic on her face will never leave my mind. I remember my mind screaming as we came flying down. I knew I was going to hear about this ride. Stan Checketts would like to hear about it too. Checketts invents amusement park rides for a living.

_____ Seventy-five percent of all people attending amusement parks enjoy the tallest rides the most. Only eighteen percent of all amusement parks have very many tall rides. Based on these statistics, Stan Checketts has a big job ahead of him. He invents amusement park rides.

_____ Think back to a time when you were on a roller coaster ride. Picture the look that must have been in your eyes. Imagine what you were thinking at the time. Imagine what you would tell the person who invented the ride. Stan Checketts just might be that person. Checketts invents amusement park rides for a living.

_____ How did it feel the last time you dropped 240 feet? Can you remember the adrenaline rush you had as you came screaming downward? Do wish you could have that experience again and again? Stan Checketts hopes that you do. Checketts invents amusement park rides.

Graphic Development

Directions: Read the following information and use the pictograph to answer the questions below.

Swoosh! What a thrill! What is your favorite amusement park ride? Amusement parks dot the United States and bring thrills and chills to kids and adults alike. The graph below shows the favorite amusement park rides of students in Mrs. Johnson's fourth-grade class.

Favorite Rides in Mrs. Johnson's Class

Power Tower	☆ ☆ ☆ ☆ ☆ ☆ ☆ ☆
Merry Go Round	☆ ☆ ☆ ☆
Roller Coaster	☆ ☆ ☆ ☆ ☆
Big Shot	☆ ☆ ☆ ☆ ☆
Tea Cups	☆ ☆ ☆

☆ = 1 student

---

1. What does each star represent?

   _____

2. How many people chose the Power Tower as their favorite ride?

   _____

3. What ride was chosen the least by the students?

   _____

4. How many students' responses are shown on the pictograph?

   _____

5. Which amusement ride was chosen by ten students?

   _____

Sentence Comprehension

Directions: Read the following sentence carefully and answer the questions below "True" (T) or "False" (F).

Rangers tried to control the growth by slaughtering older elephants and then moving the young elephants to other parks and reserves.

---

1. There was a growth problem with the elephants. _____

2. The younger elephants were slaughtered. _____

3. The rangers had to train older elephants. _____

4. Families of elephants were divided up. _____

5. The young elephants were moved to other parks. _____

Word Study

Directions: Match the pronunciations in Column A with the correct word in Column B.

Hluhluwe-Umfolozi

What?! That is a hard word to pronounce. Fortunately, there is a pronunciation included for this word. Hluhluwe-Umfolozi [Slush-looey   Oom-fall-o-zee] is a park in southeastern South Africa. The pronunciation of each word can be found in a dictionary. The pronunciation is found immediately following the word. You will find the pronunciation key in the bottom right corner of each dictionary page.

Column A	**Column B**
1. \spär' kel\	spat
2. \spăt\	sparrow
3. \spēk\	spark
4. \spärk\	sparkle
5. \spăr'ō\	speak

Paragraph Comprehension

Directions: Read the paragraph below and answer the following questions.

"The whole thing has much to do with the setup of elephant society," says South African zoologist Marian Garai. Elephants normally live in tight-knit groups. Older males keep young bulls in line. But no such role models were provided for the orphans from Kruger. Garai believes this upset the young elephants and led them to lash out at rhinos.

---

1. How do older bulls help younger bulls?

    a. They show them how to hunt.

    b. They keep younger bulls in line.

    c. They demonstrate how to eat.

    d. They carry them over rough terrain.

2. In which country is the problem with the elephants?

    a. Namibia

    b. Botswana

    c. Zimbabwe

    d. South Africa

3. What are the orphans at Kruger lacking?

    a. enough nutrients in their diet

    b. safe surroundings in which to live

    c. older elephants as role models

    d. their mothers

4. What did the elephants do to the rhinos?

    a. They lashed out at some of the rhinos.

    b. They included them in their family groups.

    c. They have taken over their territory.

    d. They have protected the rhinos.

5. Elephants normally

    a. live in clans.

    b. live in tight-knit groups.

    c. eat plants and vegetables.

    d. fight each other.

Whole Story Comprehension

Directions: Read the story below and answer the questions on the following page.

Bullies in the Park!

The trouble started about three years ago. Nearly every month, rangers in Pilanesberg National Park in northwestern South Africa would find an endangered white rhinoceros that had been killed. Then the same thing started happening at another park in southeastern South Africa.

Rhinos are sometimes hunted for their valuable horns. But no one had touched the horns of these animals. Their wounds hadn't come from guns.

The rangers who solved the crime were surprised to learn what was to blame. Young male elephants behaved badly because they had grown up without the attention of caring adults.

Several years ago, the population of elephants in South Africa's Kruger National Park was growing too large. Rangers tried to control the growth by slaughtering older elephants and then moving the younger elephants to other parks and reserves. Since 1976, almost 1,500 orphans—600 of them males, or bulls—have been moved to unfamiliar locations, where they grew up without older elephants around them.

Moving the orphans helped preserve an endangered species. But it changed the elephants' social order.

"The whole thing has much to do with the setup of elephant society," says South African zoologist Marian Garai. Elephants normally live in tight-knit groups. Older males keep young bulls in line. But no such role models were provided for the orphans from Kruger. Garai believes this upset the young elephants and led them to lash out at rhinos.

"Elephants are complex and intelligent creatures," explain Garai. "They aren't immune to stress."

What can be done? Some rangers believe the elephant bullies need foster parents. When two adult female circus elephants were returned to Pilanesberg in 1979, the nervous orphans settled down.

Now officials hope a similar plan will work for the rhino-bashing bulls. Kruger Park will move entire families of elephants to new homes instead of killing the elders and hauling away their young, and a few 40-year-old male elephants will be moved to Pilanesberg.

Preserving families may be the key to raising well-behaved elephants. Meanwhile, South Africa's white rhinos had better watch out.

Whole Story Comprehension *(cont.)*

Directions: After you have read the story on the previous page, answer the questions below.

1. When did the trouble with the rhinos begin?

    a. five years ago

    b. three years ago

    c. fifteen years ago

    d. a little over a year ago

2. Exactly what was the problem at the park in South Africa?

    a. They were running out of food for the animals.

    b. They were having to shut down the park.

    c. They were unable to locate some of the elephants.

    d. They would periodically find white rhinos that had been killed.

3. The rangers were surprised

    a. to learn how easy it was to teach the elephants to behave.

    b. to learn the young male elephants were to blame.

    c. to learn that rhinos and elephants get along.

    d. to learn that the rivers were drying up in the park.

4. What did experts say the reason was for the angry elephants?

    a. They said it was because of the overcrowding.

    b. They said it was a result of not enough food.

    c. They said it was because there were no role models for the young elephants.

    d. They said it was because of the terrain in the parks.

5. Elephants are considered

    a. large and clumsy.

    b. creatures with low intelligence.

    c. complex and intelligent creatures.

    d. creatures with low immune deficiencies.

6. Since 1976

    a. there have been 1,500 elephant orphans.

    b. there have been 600 elephant orphans.

    c. there have been 1,500 rhino attacks.

    d. there have been 1,978 rhino orphans.

7. What happened when the two circus elephants returned to Pilanesburg?

    a. The circus elephants had to be protected.

    b. The younger elephants became angry.

    c. The younger elephants settled down.

    d. The attacks on rhinos increased.

8. What do experts believe is the key to raising well-behaved elephants?

    a. provide circus elephants as role models

    b. preserve elephant families

    c. teach elephants self defense

    d. keep elephants separated

Enrichment

Directions: Read the information below and use it to answer the following questions.

Have you ever thought of elephants as angry orphans? Have you thought of an elephant as a bully? Have you ever thought of an older elephant as a role model? The article, "Bullies in the Park," uses personification to make its point.

Personification is a form of figurative language that gives an object, idea, or animal the characteristics of a person. Stating that an elephant is an orphan or a bully makes the elephant seem more like a person. Read the examples of personification below:

- The cat marched her way to the front of the house.

- The bird signaled the rest of the birds to sing at the same time.

- The floor groaned as the cheerleaders jumped onto it.

- The thought of becoming a teacher almost leaped out of my chest.

Circle only the sentences below that are examples of personification.

1. The sound of the alarm clock was shouting in my ear.

2. The elephant ate his food slowly.

3. The older elephant sat by the younger elephants.

4. The wind whispered through the trees of the jungle.

5. The tree stood firmly in its place.

6. Without adult attention, the elephants are suffering.

7. The rain drops danced on the leaves of the trees.

8. The elephant orphan angrily threw a fit.

Graphic Development

Directions: Read the following information and use the map below to answer the questions.

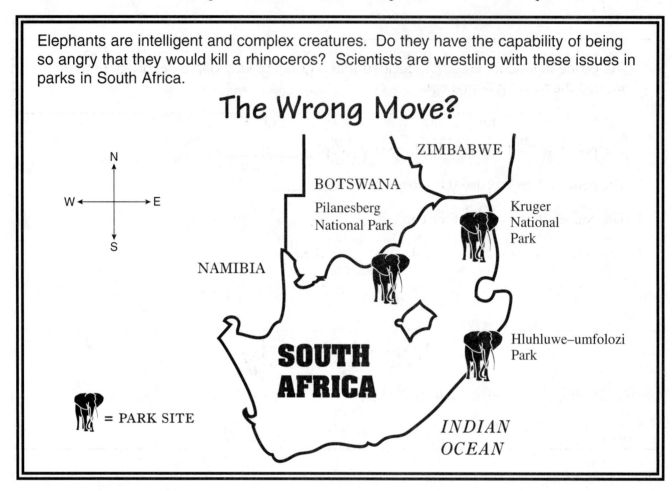

Elephants are intelligent and complex creatures. Do they have the capability of being so angry that they would kill a rhinoceros? Scientists are wrestling with these issues in parks in South Africa.

The Wrong Move?

1. How many national parks are located in South Africa?

   _____

2. What does the elephant symbol represent?

   _____

3. What is the title of this map?

   _____

4. What are the three countries that border South Africa?

   _____

5. Which park is located in the southeast of South Africa?

   _____

Sentence Comprehension

Directions: Read the following sentence carefully and answer the questions below "True" (T) or "False" (F).

> The police in Macon, Georgia, decided that a group of kids with a history of problems needed their own full-time cop.

1. The police decided a group of kids needed a cop. _____

2. The police officer arrested this group of kids. _____

3. The police officer is a full-time cop. _____

4. The kids in this neighborhood had a history of problems. _____

5. The police in Macon, Georgia, were giving up on this group of kids. _____

Word Study

Directions: Read the example in the box below and write the acronyms for the following organizations:

> **Y.E.S.**
>
> The acronym Y.E.S. stands for Youth Enrichment Services in the article about Officer Sinclair. An acronym is a word formed by the first letter of words in a phrase.

1. _____ Federal Bureau of Investigation

2. _____ Drug Abuse Resistance Education

3. _____ Central Intelligence Agency

4. _____ International Business Machines

5. _____ Internal Revenue Service

6. _____ National Aeronautics and Space Administration

Paragraph Comprehension

Directions: Read the paragraph below and answer the following questions.

> Each week, Officer Sinclair talks to the principal of Appling Middle School to check the students' grades and behavior. He meets with the kids twice a week and listens to them anytime they want to talk. In the summer, the group will go camping, tour a dairy farm, and perform service projects.

1. Each week, Officer Sinclair checks on the

    a. home life of each student.

    b. behavior and grades of the students.

    c. arrest reports of the students.

    d. amount of kids involved in after school programs.

2. What are some of the things the group will do in the summer?

    a. paint neighborhood houses

    b. go camping and roller blading

    c. tour a dairy farm and go repelling

    d. go camping and tour a dairy farm

3. Officer Sinclair shows support by

    a. meeting with the kids twice a week to talk and listen.

    b. living in the students' homes.

    c. teaching at the school.

    d. preparing the students for police training.

4. The students attend

    a. a private school.

    b. Appling High School.

    c. Appling Middle School.

    d. Appling Charter School.

5. Students will have an opportunity to

    a. live with Officer Sinclair.

    b. ride in Officer Sinclair's police car.

    c. perform service projects as a group.

    d. complete the school courses in self esteem.

Whole Story Comprehension

Directions: Read the story below and answer the questions on the following page.

Policeman Next Door

Officer Ellis Sinclair has 33 kids. Sort of. As part of a crime-prevention program, he keeps a close watch on 33 kids, ages 10 to 14. How close? He's moved right into their tough neighborhood!

The police in Macon, Georgia, decided that a group of kids with a history of problems needed their own full-time cop. So the department bought a yellow brick house in East Macon where Sinclair could live and work. He packed everything, even his prized collection of model police cars, and moved in. "The people were glad to see me," he says.

Each week, Officer Sinclair talks to the principal of Appling Middle School to check the students' grades and behavior. He meets with the kids twice a week and listens to them anytime they want to talk. In the summer, the group will go camping, tour a dairy farm, and perform service projects.

The best news: Project Y.E.S. (for Youth Enrichment Services) really seems to work. Last year, 88% of the kids in the project had been in trouble with the law. Just 8% have been in trouble since the beginning of the project, and the overall crime rate in East Macon has been lower, too.

A group of neighbors, including Sinclair's own grandmother, helps run Project Y.E.S. They say they feel safer having Sinclair nearby, so they want to help him do his job well. But Sinclair says his work is more than a job. He feels responsible for helping those 33 have a better life. Says the officer, who has no kids of his own: "They're my family."

Whole Story Comprehension *(cont.)*

Directions: After you have read the story on the previous page, answer the questions below.

1. Officer Sinclair moved into

    a. a model police car.

    b. Appling Middle School.

    c. a house bought by the police department.

    d. an apartment building.

2. What is the age range of children involved in the project?

    a. 10–18

    b. 10–14

    c. 8–16

    d. 10–20

3. Y.E.S. is a

    a. program for runaway teens.

    b. program for violent teens.

    c. crime-prevention program.

    d. drug-prevention program.

4. What does Y.E.S. stand for?

    a. Youth Ever Success

    b. Youth Equality Services

    c. Youth Enrichment Services

    d. Youth Environmental Services

5. Who helps run Project Y.E.S.?

    a. a group of neighbors, including Officer Sinclair's grandmother

    b. a group of police officers

    c. parents and teachers

    d. the D.A.R.E. officers

6. The overall crime rate in Macon, Georgia is

    a. increasing.

    b. exhilarating.

    c. decreasing.

    d. staying the same.

7. Last year, 88% of the kids were in trouble with the law; now only

    a. the boys are in trouble with the law.

    b. 8% of the kids are in trouble with the law.

    c. half of the kids are in trouble with the law.

    d. 2/3 of the kids are in trouble with the law.

8. How does Officer Sinclair feel about the 33 kids?

    a. He is frustrated with their choices.

    b. He is overwhelmed.

    c. He is tired of dealing with them.

    d. He considers them family.

Enrichment

Directions: Read the information below and use it to answer the following questions.

In the article, you learned how one man is making a difference in the lives of 33 students. Because of Project Y.E.S. (Youth Enrichment Services), and because of the support and role-modeling of Officer Sinclair, students are learning to make better choices. How does reaching out to troubled youth make a difference with crime prevention?

Getting youth involved not only makes a difference in the life of youth, it also makes a difference in communities. Community service programs designed and led by youth teach specific skills and prevent delinquency by providing opportunities for young people to bond with and improve their communities. The key to success lies in youth participation in designing, selecting, and implementing projects.

Programs like Project Y.E.S. tap into the energy and creativity of young people to make positive changes in their communities. Youth are given the opportunity to carry out projects they've designed to meet their communities' most urgent needs.

Project Y.E.S. also teaches alternatives to violence and delinquency, and teaches a sense of control over one's life, a sense of altruism, and with the help of a consistent presence of a caring adult like Officer Sinclair, builds self-esteem, optimism, and faith in the future. Role models like Officer Sinclair may be some of the only adults youth interact with that are positive individuals.

---

1. Besides helping the youth, what else is helped by community service projects?

   _____

2. What does Project Y.E.S. teach students other than a sense of altruism, self control, and self-esteem?

   _____

3. What do role models like Officer Sinclair build for students?

   _____

4. What do the letters Y.E.S. stand for?

   _____

Graphic Development

Directions: Read the following information and use the fictional circle graph below to answer the questions below.

Officer Sinclair has made a big difference in the neighborhood in Macon, Georgia. Crime rates have declined and the number of students in trouble with the law has also declined. Officer Sinclair's dedication to the community is paying off. This summer will bring good things to the neighborhood as well. Students will be filling their time with activities and experiences of a lifetime.

Super Summer Activities

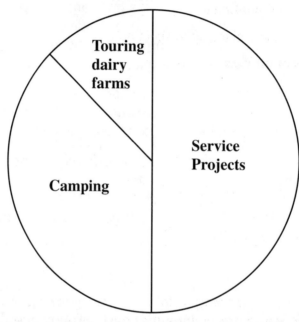

1. What are all the activities that students will be doing this summer?

_____

2. With which activity will students be spending half of their time?

_____

3. What is the title of this graph?

_____

4. Which activity will take the least amount of time?

_____

5. What activity do you think will be the most popular from the students' perspective?

_____

Sentence Comprehension

Directions: Read the following sentence carefully and answer the questions below "True" (T) or "False" (F).

> Squidzilla is amazing to scientists because it's the most complete and best-preserved giant squid specimen in the world.

1. The scientists think squidzilla is amazing. _____

2. Squidzilla was not very well preserved. _____

3. Squidzilla is the most complete giant squid specimen. _____

4. Squidzilla is many parts of different squids. _____

5. Squidzilla is still alive. _____

Word Study

Directions: Read the following information and then change the present tense verbs in the sentences below to past tense verbs.

> **wrapped**
>
> Wrapped means covered by winding or folding. The word wrapped is a verb in the past tense. Past tense verbs are actions that have already been completed or took place at a particular time in the past.

1. _____ I *find* the dog in the garage.

2. _____ We *open* the store at 6:00 A.M. yesterday.

3. _____ Scientists *look* at the squid specimen last week.

4. _____ They never *succeed* in finding another squid.

5. _____ The doctor *complete* the exam by lunchtime.

6. _____ The group *wait* for the news to come out.

7. _____ He wanted the squid specimen *chain* up.

8. _____ No one *wants* the specimen to be ruined.

Paragraph Comprehension

Directions: Read the paragraph below and answer the following questions.

The squid is in such great shape thanks to quick-thinking fishermen who found it off the coast of New Zealand. When the dead squid landed in one of their giant nets, they froze it right away so the body wouldn't rot. Then it was flown to New York and allowed to defrost overnight at the museum. Next, scientists put it in a bath of special, smelly chemicals to preserve it.

---

1. Which of the following is a true statement?

    a. The squid is in poor shape.

    b. The squid is in good shape because of the scientists.

    c. The squid is in good shape thanks to some quick-thinking fishermen.

    d. The squid is in good shape thanks to squidzilla.

2. Where was the dead squid located?

    a. It was in a fossilized cave.

    b. It landed in a giant net.

    c. It got caught in a rudder.

    d. It was killed in a boat collision.

3. Why did the fishermen freeze the squid?

    a. so it wouldn't rot

    b. because there wasn't enough room in the boat

    c. so it wouldn't fight back

    d. because it was the law

4. The squid was flown to

    a. New Jersey.

    b. New York.

    c. the Smithsonian Museum.

    d. Washington, D.C.

5. What was used to preserve the giant squid specimen?

    a. a base

    b. an acid

    c. a special shampoo

    d. a smelly chemical

Whole Story Comprehension

Directions: Read the story below and answer the questions on the following page.

Monster of the Deep

It lies, still and wet, in a huge metal tank wrapped with chains. The case is so big it cannot fit through any of the doors in New York City's American Museum of Natural History. On the side of the case, someone has scratched the letters, "S-Q-U-I-D-Z-I-L-L-A."

"We keep it chained up so it doesn't get out," jokes Neil Landman, a scientist at the museum. There is no way the creature inside that case could get out: it's dead. But what exactly is it?

It's a giant squid, one of the earth's most mysterious animals. No one has ever seen a live giant squid. Scientists have been able to study only a few body parts that have washed up from the ocean over the years.

Squidzilla is amazing to scientists because it's the most complete and best-preserved giant squid specimen in the world. All eight arms are in place!

The squid is in such great shape thanks to quick-thinking fishermen who found it off the coast of New Zealand. When the dead squid landed in one of their giant nets, they froze it right away so the body wouldn't start to rot. Then it was flown to New York and allowed to defrost overnight at the museum. Next, the scientists put it in a bath of special, smelly chemicals to preserve it.

At a length of 25 feet and a weight of 200 pounds, it looked at first to museum scientists like a baby giant squid. Its tentacles are much shorter than those found in the past. Scientists think the biggest giant squid may be as long as 60 feet and weigh more than a ton! But after studying the squid, Landman concluded that it was a full-grown male. "All the other, larger specimens have been female," Landman says. "For the first time, we can infer that there is a difference in size between the males and females."

Giant squid have never been observed in the ocean because they swim in very deep waters—probably as far down as 3,000 feet.

Scientists aren't sure how many of them exist or where in the world the others may live. Don't hold your breath waiting for answers. "Anyone who has gone out to see a giant squid has never succeeded," says Landman. "It is an elusive animal."

Whole Story Comprehension *(cont.)*

Directions: After you have read the story on the previous page, answer the questions below.

1. What is Squidzilla?

    a. a monster

    b. a giant squid specimen

    c. a live female squid

    d. a mysterious unknown animal

2. Squidzilla is kept at

    a. the Metropolitan Museum of Arts.

    b. the Smithsonian.

    c. the American Museum of Natural History.

    d. the Oceanic Museum.

3. The amazing part of the squid specimen is

    a. the fact that it is the largest ever found.

    b. that it is still alive.

    c. that the squid was frozen.

    d. that all eight arms are in place.

4. Why have giant squids never been seen?

    a. They are lost.

    b. They are extinct.

    c. They swim in very deep waters.

    d. They are sensitive to the sun.

5. What was the sequence of how the squid was handled?

    a. The squid landed in a net, the fishermen froze the squid, the squid was flown to New York, and then was bathed in a special chemical.

    b. The fishermen froze the squid, the squid was flown to New York, then was bathed in a special chemical, and the squid landed in the net.

    c. The squid landed in a net, the fishermen froze the squid, the squid was bathed in a special chemical, and then the squid was flown to New York.

    d. The squid was immediately flown to New York where it was bathed in chemical. Then they discovered the squid in a net.

6. A squid is considered

    a. an elusive animal.

    b. an endangered animal.

    c. food for killer whales.

    d. fish bait.

7. What have scientists inferred about female squids in comparison to male squids?

    a. They are extinct.

    b. They prefer shallow waters.

    c. They are frozen soon after death.

    d. They are larger in size.

8. Which of the following statements is a fact about squids?

    a. Giant squids are beautiful creatures.

    b. A female squid is 20 to 30 feet longer in length than a male squid.

    c. Giant squids look like monsters.

    d. Giant squids need to be chained up.

Enrichment

Directions: Read the information below and use it to answer the following questions.

What do we know about the giant squid? There really isn't a lot of information because the giant squid is an elusive animal. Read these facts about the giant squid:

• Where does the giant squid live?

Few giant squid have ever been seen because they live almost a mile below the surface of the water. Giant squids prefer the deep, cold sea and probably live as far down as 3,000 feet. Warm water causes the squid to rise to the surface and not be able to get down. This is probably why the squid has been so elusive to humans!

• What does the giant squid eat?

Giant squids are carnivores, or meat eaters, and eat fish, other squid, and some have even been known to eat whales. The giant squid has a parrot-like beak that is used to rip chunks of flesh from its prey.

• What is the body of a giant squid like?

A giant squid is the largest invertebrate. It has a long torpedo-shaped body. A squid has eight arms, or tentacles, and is in the same family as the octopus. Males have been known to be as long as 25 feet and females as long as 60 feet. A squid also has the largest eyes in the animal kingdom. The eyes can be as long as 18 inches across.

• How long do giant squids live?

Giant squids have short life cycles, most of them reaching maturity in one to two years. Females grow larger and live longer.

1. What does a giant squid eat?

   _____

2. About how long do male and female squids get?

   _____

3. The giant squid has the largest eyes in the animal kingdom and is also the largest what?

   _____

4. What does the giant squid use to kill its prey?

   _____

5. What does warm water do to the giant squid?

   _____

Graphic Development

Directions: Use the chart below to answer the questions about large animals of the sea.

Squidzilla has been found! Scientists have determined that female giant squids are longer than male giant squids. The squid in the article was 25 feet long and all eight arms were in place. This is pretty amazing to scientists. Squidzilla is perhaps the largest squid specimen ever found. But is it the largest animal of the sea?

Large Animals of the Sea

Whale shark	
Blue whale	
Killer whale	
Giant squid (male)	
Humpback whale	

0   10   20   30   40   50   60   70   80   90   100 ft.

Measurement in approximate feet

1. What is the largest animal of the sea?

   _____

2. How long is the killer whale?

   _____

3. What is the title of the chart?

   _____

4. Scientists believe that a female giant squid can get as long as 60 feet. How long does a male giant squid get?

   _____

5. What length is the whale shark?

   _____

Sentence Comprehension

Directions: Read the following sentence carefully and answer the questions below "True" (T) or "False" (F).

> Computer artists created a golden underwater city, lots of weird-looking aliens, amazing space scenes, and Queen Amidala's wild outfits and hairdos.

1. Computer artists filmed amazing space scenes in outer space. _____

2. The underwater city is made of silver. _____

3. Queen Amidala's outfits and hairdos are boring. _____

4. There are plenty of weird-looking aliens. _____

5. Computer artists created an underwater city. _____

Word Study

Directions: Read the following information and write the antonym for each of the words below.

> **Antonyms**
>
> *"good* over *evil . . ."* These words are opposites. Words that have opposite meanings are antonyms. Antonyms are useful when clarifying thoughts or making comparisons.

1. _____ cold

2. _____ dry

3. _____ soft

4. _____ light

5. _____ strong

6. _____ day

7. _____ short

8. _____ brave

9. _____ good

10. _____ under

11. _____ down

12. _____ out

Paragraph Comprehension

Directions: Read the paragraph below and answer the following questions.

In 1977, audiences first met Luke Skywalker, Princess Leia, Han Solo, and bad, old Darth Vader. Fans went crazy! They ran to see *Star Wars* again and again. Then they rushed to see what happened next in *The Empire Strikes Back* and *Return of the Jedi*. The films made nearly $2 billion in theaters around the world and even more in toy sales.

1. What was the response of fans to *Star Wars?*

   a. negative

   b. mediocre

   c. Fans seemed to like it.

   d. Fans went crazy.

2. What was the sequel to *Star Wars?*

   a. *Return of the Jedi*

   b. *Empire Strikes Back*

   c. *Phantom Menace*

   d. *Star Wars II*

3. How much money did the films make in theaters around the world?

   a. nearly a million dollars

   b. nearly two million dollars

   c. nearly two billion dollars

   d. over 200 million dollars

4. Who were some of the characters in *Star Wars?*

   a. Luke Skywalker and Darth Vader

   b. Queen Amidala and Princess Leia

   c. Jar Jar Binks and Han Solo

   d. Princess Leia and Darth Maul

5. What year did *Star Wars* come out?

   a. 1877

   b. 1977

   c. 1978

   d. 1997

Whole Story Comprehension

Directions: Read the story below and answer the questions on the following page.

Feel the Force

In 1977, audiences first met Luke Skywalker, Princess Leia, Han Solo, and bad, old Darth Vader. Fans went crazy! They ran to see *Star Wars* again and again. Then they rushed to see what happened next in *The Empire Strikes Back* and *Return of the Jedi*. The films made nearly $2 billion in theaters around the world and even more in toy sales.

So the films' creator, George Lucas, decided to take fans back in time before *Star Wars*. *Star Wars: Episode 1—The Phantom Menace* takes place 30 years earlier. Luke and Leia are not born. But we see their mother, the young Queen Amidala, whose kingdom is threatened by the evil warrior, Darth Maul. Their father, Darth Vader, is just an angel-faced kid named Anakin Skywalker. But he shows signs of the Force, the mysterious energy that Jedi knights can control.

The movie is packed with special effects. It has nearly four times as many as *Titanic*. Computer artists created a golden underwater city, lots of weird looking aliens, amazing space scenes, and Queen Amidala's wild outfits and hairdos. The film cost more than $115 million and took four years to complete.

Fans couldn't wait! Some lined up at theaters two months before tickets went on sale. Many had already read the movie's script on the Internet where there were hundreds of Web sites about *Phantom Menace*.

Toy stores were ready for the rush, too. Hasbro created 100 action figures, plus other toys, based on the film. Hasbro will make the toys for Episodes II and III also. The company is expected to earn $5 billion from *Star Wars* toys in the next 10 years.

George Lucas makes no apologies for selling *Star Wars* toys. He says the movies' struggles between good and evil are important for kids to think about. He has three kids of his own. He hopes his films will help young people see that choosing good over evil every day makes them heroic. "Heroes come in all sizes," he says. "You can be a very small hero."

Whole Story Comprehension *(cont.)*

Directions: After you have read the story on the previous page, answer the questions below.

1. When does *Phantom Menace* take place?

    a. 20 years after Star Wars

    b. 30 years before *Star Wars*

    c. 10 years after *Empire Strikes Back*

    d. a sequel to *Star Wars*

2. Who is Anakin Skywalker?

    a. Darth Vader as a boy

    b. Luke Skywalker's son

    c. Jar Jar Binks' hero

    d. Princess Leia's brother

3. The film cost more than $115 million and

    a. went over its budget.

    b. took five years to complete.

    c. took four years to complete.

    d. none of the above

4. *Star Wars* has made its way into the

    a. stock market.

    b. food industry.

    c. grocery stores.

    d. toy industry.

5. *Phantom Menace* has four times

    a. the amount of violence than in other movies.

    b. as many special effects as *Titanic*.

    c. as many characters as *Gunsmoke*.

    d. as many sound effects as *Titanic*.

6. Hasbro is

    a. the toy company that makes *Star Wars* toys.

    b. the title of the next *Star Wars* movie.

    c. the *Phantom Menace*.

    d. Han Solo's father.

7. Which of the following statements is a fact?

    a. The *Star Wars* movies are cool!

    b. The *Star Wars* movies are liked by everyone.

    c. The *Phantom Menace* is the first of three new *Star Wars* movies.

    d. Darth Vader is the most popular of the characters.

8. George Lucas believes

    a. the characters are real.

    b. the *Star Wars* series is boring.

    c. heroes aren't important anymore.

    d. heroes come in all sizes.

118

Enrichment

Directions: Read the information below and use it to answer the following questions.

Have you ever missed a word on a spelling test because you forgot to capitalize it? Capitalization is considered one of the mechanics of writing. The article you just read had many examples of when to use a capital letter. "Feel the Force" capitalized names of people, characters, titles of movies, names of companies, and the beginning words of each sentence. Use the following guidelines to help you remember when to capitalize and when not to capitalize.

Capitalize

- Names of People
- Proper Nouns
- Proper Adjectives
- Historical Events
- Names of a Specific Course
- All Languages, Races, Religions
- Organizations

- Abbreviations
- First Word in a Quotation
- Sections of the Country
- Words/Titles Used as Names
- Titles
- Official Names
- Days of the Week/Month First word in a sentence

---

1. Should you capitalize the title of a newspaper?

   _____

2. Should you capitalize the sections of the country?

   _____

3. What parts of speech should be capitalized?

   _____

4. In using quotations, which words in the sentence should be capitalized?

   _____

Graphic Development

Directions: Read the following information and use the Venn diagram to answer the questions below.

Star Wars movies have made their mark! The enthusiasm for weird aliens and the mysterious energy that only Jedi knights can control, has made a comeback. The latest of movies is *Episode I—The Phantom Menace.* Just what are the similarities and differences between this new flick and the original?

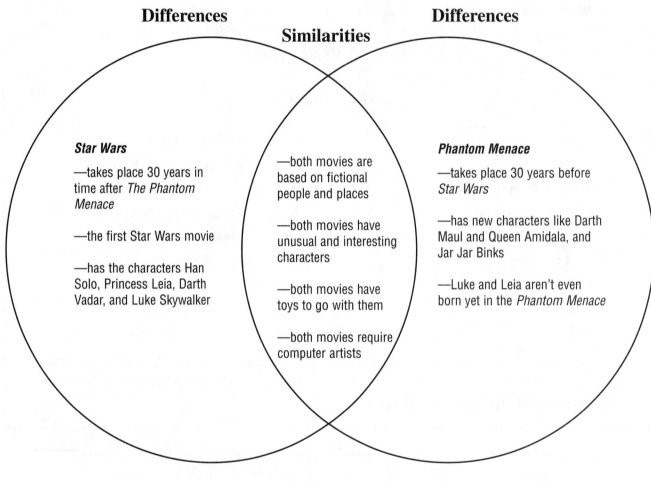

Differences   **Similarities**   **Differences**

Star Wars

—takes place 30 years in time after *The Phantom Menace*

—the first Star Wars movie

—has the characters Han Solo, Princess Leia, Darth Vadar, and Luke Skywalker

—both movies are based on fictional people and places

—both movies have unusual and interesting characters

—both movies have toys to go with them

—both movies require computer artists

Phantom Menace

—takes place 30 years before *Star Wars*

—has new characters like Darth Maul and Queen Amidala, and Jar Jar Binks

—Luke and Leia aren't even born yet in the *Phantom Menace*

1. What information can be gathered from this Venn diagram?

_____

2. What are two of the similarities between the two movies?

_____

3. Which movie has the character of Queen Amidala?

_____

4. Both movies require what type of artist to be used?

_____

5. Which movie has toys to go with the movie characters?

_____

Sentence Comprehension

Directions: Read the following sentence carefully and answer the questions below "True" (T) or "False" (F).

Kids also love to laugh, and *Goosebumps* episodes make kids laugh through a thrill of fear.

1. Episodes of *Goosebumps* are for adults only. _____

2. Kids love to laugh. _____

3. *Goosebumps* episodes just scare kids. _____

4. *Goosebumps* is a new video game. _____

5. *Goosebumps* episodes are meant to scare and entertain. _____

Word Study

Directions: Read the following information and write an adjective from the box to describe the noun in each sentence below.

vicious

In the article, the beast was described as vicious. Vicious means dangerously aggressive. Beast is a noun and vicious is an adjective. An adjective is a word that describes the noun.

enormous	wicked	fun	cute	small	new

1. The _____ beast could barely fit through the door.

2. There is only a _____ piece of pie left.

3. The kids that read the books say they are _____ books to read.

4. The _____ nightmare wasn't the same as the others.

5. All of the kids ran after the _____ little puppy.

6. Eddie and Sue met up with a _____ witch in the story as well.

Paragraph Comprehension

Directions: Read the paragraph below and answer the following questions.

Not convinced? Just listen! Imagine going with Sue and Eddie for a "Night in Terror Tower." As their parents attend a meeting at the hotel, these 13- and 11-year-olds tour London. The kids look forward to the tour bus stop at Terror Tower. This tower was a prison and torture chamber during the Middle Ages.

---

1. "Night in Terror Tower" is probably

    a. the name of a store.

    b. the title of a book.

    c. a nightmare.

    d. the sequel to a movie.

2. How old are Eddie and Sue?

    a. 6 and 8

    b. 9 and 11

    c. 11 and 13

    d. 14 and 16

3. Sue and Eddie are looking forward to

    a. getting home.

    b. touring Terror Tower.

    c. going on vacation.

    d. school starting up again.

4. Where are their parents?

    a. they stayed home

    b. they are lost in Terror Tower

    c. attending a meeting in the hotel

    d. lost

5. What was Terror Tower?

    a. the name of a book

    b. the tallest part of a haunted house

    c. part of Eddie and Sue's dream

    d. a torture chamber during the Middle Ages

Whole Story Comprehension

Directions: Read the story below and answer the questions on the following page.

Goosebumps TV

If you are like most kids, you like to read *Goosebumps* and you love TV. If this describes you, you won't want to miss watching the TV episodes of R.L. Stine's *Goosebumps* stories.

Stine is the Pied Piper of children. His books have attracted millions of young readers. In fact, R.L. Stine titles sell over a million copies a month! The magic carries over to TV. What is it about these stories that makes them irresistible?

Kids love to be scared and Stine's tales are scary. Kids also love to laugh, and *Goosebumps* episodes make kids laugh through a thrill of fear. They are filled with turns, surprises, and funny jokes. Unlike most TV programs, *Goosebumps* endings are unpredictable.

The combination of mystery, horror, and adventure is enough to grab any kid's interest. And your parents can relax. The episodes are designed to give shivers, not nightmares. The scares are mild-mannered.

Not convinced? Just listen! Imagine going with Sue and Eddie for a "Night in Terror Tower." As their parents attend a meeting at the hotel, these 13- and 11-year olds tour London. The kids look forward to the tour bus stop at Terror Tower. This tower was a prison and torture chamber during the Middle Ages.

At the tower, however, strange things begin to happen that only Eddie and Sue can see. The figures begin to move as if real. The only children on the tour are also the only ones to hear the ghostly warnings. Then the guide tells a tale about a prince and princess sentenced to die in the tower five hundred years ago. Without warning, the children find themselves separated from the group. Stranger and more haunting things happen to Sue and Eddie as they are drawn toward the fate meant for the prince and princess.

Is that too fantastic for you? "Welcome to Camp Nightmare" brings viewers into a scene that is familiar to many kids. At first, Camp Nightmare seems like the summer camp of Billy's dreams. It has basketball, archery, and a big lake. Then really weird stuff starts happening. Billy is worried about a mysterious, vicious beast called Sabre. Fellow campers start disappearing, one by one. Mike is bitten by a snake. Roger is attacked by a creature in the woods. Then, Jay and Colin disappear in the lake. Afraid he is next, Billy is determined to find out what is going on.

These episodes, and many others, offer kids, eight and older, a hair-raisingly fun getaway. Kids are tuning in. So should you. Stine spins just as good a tale on TV as on paper.

Whole Story Comprehension *(cont.)*

Directions: After you have read the story on the previous page, answer the questions below.

1. Who is R.L. Stine?

    a. author of *Goosebumps* books

    b. character in *Goosebumps* books

    c. the father of Eddie and Sue

    d. the TV producer of *Goosebumps*

2. What age are *Goosebumps* books geared to?

    a. small children

    b. high school children

    c. kids eight and older

    d. mostly boys

3. What do kids like about the books?

    a. They have hard covers.

    b. They have free decoder rings.

    c. They are horror stories.

    d. They are a combination of mystery, horror, and adventure.

4. What happens in the "Tower of Terror"?

    a. The children hear screaming.

    b. Wax figures begin to move as though they are real.

    c. Sue and Eddie can't find their parents.

    d. Sue and Eddie find the prince and princess.

5. What happens to Billy's fellow campers at Camp Nightmare?

    a. They steal the food.

    b. They begin to disappear.

    c. They flood the tent.

    d. They get lost in the woods.

6. What makes *Goosebumps* episodes different than other TV programs?

    a. The endings are unpredictable.

    b. The endings are all the same.

    c. There are no commercials.

    d. The endings are incomplete.

7. The author, R.L. Stine,

    a. sells bookmarks to go with his books.

    b. bases his stories on real-life adventures.

    c. sells over a million copies in a month.

    d. writes a sequel to each story he writes.

8. The author of this article

    a. likes the books by R.L. Stine.

    b. thinks the *Goosebumps* books are silly.

    c. is discouraging people from reading *Goosebumps*.

    d. is warning parents of the content in R.L. Stine books.

Enrichment

Directions: Read the information below and use it to answer the following questions.

The title, *Goosebumps TV,* is actually an abbreviation! The word TV is the shortened word of the word television. Other examples of abbreviated words are CD (compact disc) and phone (telephone).

Zipf's principle is the term used for this. Zipf's principle is the shortening of words from common use, as in *ad* for *advertisement*. Words that have been shortened are now called abbreviations or clipped words. Clipped words often become more frequently used than the original words. Look at the examples below:

ad = advertisement

burger = hamburger

photo = photograph

fan = fanatic

sub = submarine

fridge = refrigerator

gym = gymnasium

tux = tuxedo

taxi = taxicab

Now look at the clipped words below. What was the original word? Write it in the space. The first one has been done for you.

1. memo   memorandum _____

2. grad   _____

3. champ   _____

4. bike   _____

5. vet   _____

6. trig   _____

7. auto   _____

8. math   _____

9. phone   _____

10. con   _____

Graphic Development

Directions: Read the following information and use the bar graph of Mr. Minket's fifth grade class to answer the questions below.

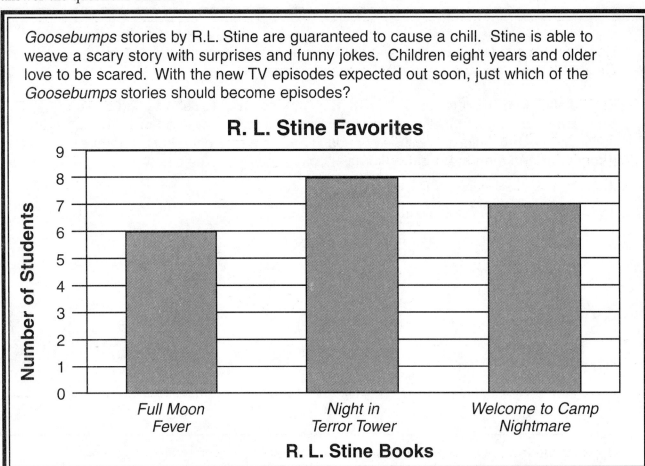

Goosebumps stories by R.L. Stine are guaranteed to cause a chill. Stine is able to weave a scary story with surprises and funny jokes. Children eight years and older love to be scared. With the new TV episodes expected out soon, just which of the *Goosebumps* stories should become episodes?

R. L. Stine Favorites

Number of Students

Full Moon Fever — 6
Night in Terror Tower — 8
Welcome to Camp Nightmare — 7

R. L. Stine Books

1. Which book did most of the students pick as their favorite R.L. Stine book?

   _____

2. What is the total number of students that are in Mr. Minket's class?

   _____

3. How many of R.L. Stine's books did students have to pick from?

   _____

4. How many more students like *Night in Terror Tower* more than *Full Moon Fever?*

   _____

5. Does this graph show the differences of opinion between male and female students?

   _____

Sentence Comprehension

Directions: Read the following sentence carefully and answer the questions below "True" (T) or "False" (F).

> However, Harry's family is more like the wicked stepmother and stepsisters of *Cinderella* than the strict parents of realistic stories.

1. Harry lives with a wicked stepmother and stepsisters. _____

2. Harry's family is similar to Cinderella's family. _____

3. Harry's story is a sequel to *Cinderella*. _____

4. Harry enjoys living with his family. _____

5. Harry's family is probably more strict than most strict parents. _____

Word Study

Directions: Read the following information and write the prefix of the words on the lines before each word.

> **unusual**
>
> Unusual means uncommon, not usual, or rare. *Unusual* begins with the common prefix, /un/. A prefix comes before the root word. Prefixes can often change the meaning of words.

1. _____ hyperactive

2. _____ interrupt

3. _____ circumstance

4. _____ catalogue

5. _____ copilot

6. _____ semicircle

7. _____ hexagon

8. _____ introduce

9. _____ intervene

10. _____ extraordinary

Paragraph Comprehension

Directions: Read the paragraph below and answer the following questions.

Harry finally escapes from his awful aunt and uncle. He is sent by friends of his parents to a school called Hogwarts. Hogwarts has unusual classes involving magic. However, it also includes strict rules and competition among students that real kids experience. The most popular game at Hogwarts is Quidditch, a kind of hockey played on flying broomsticks.

1. Harry is able to escape

    a. the Hogwarts.

    b. his aunt and uncle.

    c. his parents and friends.

    d. the Quidditch.

2. Where was Harry sent?

    a. to Hogwarts, a school

    b. to the orphanage

    c. back to his aunt and uncle's house

    d. to live with his grandfather

3. What are the classes like at Hogwarts?

    a. They are full of spoiled boys.

    b. They are taught in a foreign language.

    c. They involve magic.

    d. They are difficult to pass.

4. Quidditch is

    a. a tough course at Hogwarts.

    b. the name of the school Harry attends.

    c. Harry's last name.

    d. a game like hockey played on broomsticks.

5. How is Hogwarts similar to school that real kids experience?

    a. It has teachers.

    b. It has competition among the students.

    c. It has extracurricular activities.

    d. It has a principal.

Whole Story Comprehension

Directions: Read the story below and answer the questions on the following page.

A Review of Harry Potter and the Sorcerer's Stone

Some books are fun because they are true to life. You can easily identify with the characters. Other books take kids to an imaginary universe. From fairytales to *Alice in Wonderland* to the *Chronicles of Narnia,* they create a new world that's similar to our own, but with magical differences. A great new series of books about a boy named Harry Potter creates a fantasy world that kids will love to visit.

J.K. Rowling's first book about Harry is called *Harry Potter and the Sorcerer's Stone.* Harry lives in a place that seems in some ways like modern-day Great Britain. Harry has problems like real kids. His parents died when he was a baby. He doesn't get along with the aunt and uncle with whom he lives. His cousin is a spoiled brat and a bully. However, Harry's family is more like the wicked stepmother and stepsisters of *Cinderella* than the strict parents of realistic stories. For example, Harry's aunt and uncle give their son Dudley two bedrooms: one to sleep in and one in which to keep his extra toys. Harry has no toys and must sleep in a cupboard.

Harry, though, has magical powers. He also has some very unusual adults on his side. For example, Hagrid is a giant twice as tall as normal men. When Harry's aunt and uncle keep Harry from getting important mail about his future, Hagrid steps in.

Harry finally escapes from his awful aunt and uncle. He is sent by friends of his parents to a school called Hogwarts. Hogwarts has unusual classes involving magic. However, it also includes strict rules and competition among students that real kids experience. The most popular game at Hogwarts is Quidditch, a kind of hockey played on flying broomsticks.

Kids will root for Harry, who is brave and smart, but not perfect. Will Harry find the Sorcerer's Stone? Will his team win at Quidditch? Most importantly, will the headmaster, Albus Dumbledore, tell Harry what really happened to his parents? Kids will love the fantasy world in this book.

Whole Story Comprehension *(cont.)*

Directions: After you have read the story on the previous page, answer the questions below.

1. Harry Potter books are

   a. comic books.

   b. romance novels.

   c. fiction books.

   d. fantasy books.

2. This article is

   a. encouraging young kids to try magic.

   b. endorsing strict rules in public schools.

   c. a review of the book, *Harry Potter and the Sorcerer's Stone.*

   d. negative about Harry Potter books.

3. Who is J.K. Rowling?

   a. author of Harry Potter books

   b. publisher of Harry Potter books

   c. mother of Harry Potter

   d. fan of Harry Potter books

4. Harry lives in a place similar to

   a. a town you live in.

   b. a fantasy world.

   c. modern-day Great Britain.

   d. New York City.

5. Where does Harry sleep at his aunt's house?

   a. in the upstairs bedroom

   b. at the Quidditch

   c. in a cupboard

   d. with his cousin, Dudley

6. Harry is considered

   a. shy and quiet.

   b. brave and smart.

   c. brave, yet foolish.

   d. angry and frustrated.

7. Hagrid is

   a. Harry's roommate at Hogwart's.

   b. an enemy Harry is afraid of.

   c. a giant twice as tall as normal men.

   d. a giant out to get Harry's parents.

8. Who is Albus Dumbledore?

   a. Harry's father

   b. a wizard

   c. the sorcerer

   d. the Headmaster at Hogwarts

Enrichment

Directions: Read the information below and use it to answer the following questions.

Read these sentences taken from the article that you just read. Note the use of commas in these sentences.

However, Harry's family is more like the wicked stepmother and stepsisters of "Cinderella" than the strict parents of realistic stories.

Harry, though, has magical powers.

When Harry's aunt and uncle keep Harry from getting important mail about the future, Hagrid steps in.

Most importantly, will the headmaster, Albus Dumbledore, tell Harry what really happened to his parents?

How do you know when to use a comma? A comma is used in a series of words, to set off dialogue, and between two clauses. Look at the following examples:

Series of Words
I will bring the milk, cookies, and bread.

To set off Dialogue
The mother sat up and said, "I think I can handle that."

Between Two Clauses
After reading the note, I turned pale.

Write the reasons why commas have been used in these sentences.

1. Harry Potter was wondering what he was to do with the baking soda, clay, and food coloring.

_____

2. The game of Quidditch was taking longer than planned and Mr. Dumbledore shouted, "Time's up!"

_____

3. After waking up, Sally brushed her teeth.

_____

Graphic Development

Directions: Read the following information and use the character web to analyze the characters from Harry Potter.

J.K. Rowlings has created a wonderful world of fantasy in her series of Harry Potter. The characters and plots are complex and intriguing. Which characters are out to get Harry and which ones will offer support?

Graphic Organizer Web

1. What is the topic of the character web?

   _____

2. Who is Harry's headmaster at Hogwarts?

   _____

3. How many of the characters seem to be against Harry?

   _____

4. Name two things about the character Hagrid.

   _____

5. Who is the main character in *Harry Potter and the Sorcerer's Stone?*

   _____

Sentence Comprehension

Directions: Read the following sentence carefully and answer the questions below "True" (T) or "False" (F).

> The whales you see in zoos, aquariums, and ocean theme parks are living confined, uncomfortable lives.

1. Whales are uncomfortable living outside of their natural environment. _____

2. Whales are kept in zoos, aquariums, and ocean theme parks. _____

3. Whales are confined if they live in zoos, but not ocean theme parks. _____

4. Aquariums are the best habitats for the whales. _____

5. This sentence is about how a whale is born. _____

Word Study

Directions: Read the following information in the box. On the lines below, write only units of measurement that indicate length.

> **mile**
>
> A mile is a unit of measurement. There are many different words used to express measurement. Length, weight, capacity, volume, square measure, and land measure are all categories of measurement words. Mile is a measurement of length.

inches	yards	liters	pounds	decimeters
miles	milliliters	quarts	feet	cups
centimeters	grams	tons	gallons	kiloliters

1. _____   4. _____

2. _____   5. _____

3. _____   6. _____

Paragraph Comprehension

Directions: Read the paragraph below and answer the following questions.

> While Keiko was getting stronger, his caretakers were busy designing a new home for him in Iceland. Because Keiko had lived almost his whole life in captivity, it was too risky to just set him free. The solution was to build a giant floating pen in the North Atlantic Ocean. The pen is 250 feet long and has walls made of special nets so that fish can swim in and out. Keiko can see and hear nearby whales and birds.

1. Where was a home built for Keiko?

   a. Iceland

   b. Greenland

   c. Arctic

   d. Sea World

2. Why couldn't they just set Keiko free?

   a. They couldn't find him.

   b. He was unable to feed himself.

   c. He had lived his whole life in captivity.

   d. He was under contract with the movie producers.

3. In which ocean was the pen for Keiko built?

   a. Indian Ocean

   b. North Atlantic Ocean

   c. Arctic Ocean

   d. Pacific Ocean

4. What type of pen was built for Keiko?

   a. a glass pen so Keiko can see outside

   b. a floating pen with special nets

   c. an aquarium with heated water

   d. a large pen to fit Keiko's family

5. What can Keiko hear and see from his pen?

   a. short, high sounds

   b. whales in nearby cages

   c. nearby whales and birds

   d. his movie fans

Whole Story Comprehension

Directions: Read the story below and answer the questions on the following page.

Captivity Equals Cruelty for Whales

Most killer whales swim thousands of miles in their lifetimes. They travel long distances while hunting seals, sea lions, and dolphins. But some whales are captured and live in small pools to be observed by people. The whales you see at zoos, aquariums, and ocean theme parks are living confined, uncomfortable lives.

One whale that has lived an unnatural life of captivity is Keiko. He was the killer whale that starred in the 1993 movie *Free Willy*.

Keiko's journey began in the frosty blue waters of the Atlantic Ocean near Iceland, where he was born about 20 years ago. At age two, he was captured and taken to an aquarium in Iceland. He would never swim with his pod (family group) again.

Soon after that, he was moved to an aquarium in Canada, and began performing tricks for people. But he didn't make his big splash until an aquarium in Mexico bought him. That's where he landed the lead whale role in *Free Willy*. The hit movie made Keiko a Hollywood heavy-weight.

In the movie, Keiko's character suffers through awful living conditions in a theme park. In real life, Keiko's situation wasn't any better. His pool at the aquarium in Mexico was too small and too warm. His skin, once glossy and slick, broke out in sores. Also, the big fin on his back, called a dorsal fin, flopped sadly over to one side.

Keiko's fans rushed to his rescue. A group called the Free Willy Foundation raised enough money to fly him from Mexico to a specially built pool in Newport, Oregon, in 1996. In his new cool pool (just 45 degrees Fahrenheit), Keiko's health improved right away. His skin sores disappeared and he gained 2,000 pounds. Soon he was strong enough for a journey home.

While Keiko was getting stronger, his caretakers were busy designing a new home for him in Iceland. Because Keiko had lived almost his whole life in captivity, it was too risky just to set him free. The solution was to build a giant floating pen in the North Atlantic Ocean. The pen is 250 feet long and has walls made of special nets so that fish swim in and out. Keiko can see and hear nearby whales and birds.

Although some people think Keiko's move was stressful, he is still far more fortunate than other whales that have been captured. It is impossible to create a healthy environment for a whale in an aquarium or other home created by people. Suppose the temperature and chemical makeup of the water are carefully controlled. A pool is still too tiny to serve as the home of an animal that may way up to 10 tons. In addition, a captive animal cannot be near its natural neighbors fish— birds, and other ocean animals. It certainly cannot travel the world's oceans.

Whales are fun to observe. But the next time you see a whale in an aquarium or theme park, ask yourself this question: Is it okay to pen up a beautiful animal in an unnatural, possibly unhealthy environment so that people can look at it? Whales are among the world's most fascinating animals. Let's allow them to live peacefully in the ocean.

Whole Story Comprehension (cont.)

Directions: After you have read the story on the previous page, answer the questions below.

1. How is the life of a free killer whale different than one in captivity?

    a. They are larger whales.

    b. They are trained by trainers.

    c. They can swim thousands of miles.

    d. They are paid lots of money.

2. At what age was Keiko captured?

    a. five

    b. two

    c. four

    d. 10

3. What were the conditions like in Mexico for Keiko?

    a. frigid water

    b. too small and too warm

    c. too large and spacious

    d. small enough but water was too warm

4. Who helped Keiko?

    a. his trainer

    b. his doctor

    c. his fans with the Free Willy Foundation

    d. his movie crew

5. Where was Keiko sent to recover?

    a. Iceland

    b. Mexico

    c. Canada

    d. Newport, Oregon

6. Keiko is a

    a. whale.

    b. movie producer.

    c. famous actress.

    d. consumer.

7. Even with temperatures and climate controls,

    a. the pool was still not the best option.

    b. Keiko was able to escape.

    c. Keiko began to grow.

    d. Keiko was released.

8. How heavy can a whale get?

    a. over 500 hundred pounds

    b. up to 10 tons

    c. over 16 tons

    d. over 30,000 tons

Enrichment

Directions: Read the information below and use it to answer the following questions.

There are two different groups of whales. There are the Baleen Whales and the Toothed Whales. Baleen Whales have baleen which are used to sieve food from the seawater. These types of whales are considered filter feeders. Here are three types of Baleen Whales.

Blue Whale—A Blue Whale is the largest animal and the largest whale. A Blue Whale is a pale blue-gray in color and has a long streamlined body. Blue Whales are often found alone or in pairs. There are approximately 6,000 to 14,000 Blue Whales, and they are on the endangered species list. Blue Whales eat krill or other crustaceans.

Humpback Whale—Humpback whales can dive for three to nine minutes and have a pronounced hump in front of their fin on top. There is approximately 12,000–15,000 in the Humpback Whale population. Humpback Whales can weigh 25–30 tons and eat krill and other crustaceans.

Minke Whale—The population of Minke Whales is approximately 500,000 to one million. Minke Whales group into sizes of one on up to 100 at good feeding sites. Minke whales are a pale-gray/bluish-gray color with white on the under side. Minke Whales have been seen swimming alongside a boat.

Toothed Whales have teeth and eat their food with teeth instead of with baleen. Here are two Toothed whales.

Killer Whale—Keiko, from the article, is a Killer Whale. Another name for a Killer Whale is an Orca. Killer Whales eat fish, and occasionally squid and octopus. Killer Whales live in pods of groups from three to 25. Killer Whales have teeth which curve back toward the throat. Killer Whales can travel up to 34 mph.

Bottlenose Dolphin—Bottlenose dolphins are whales and are powerful swimmers and divers. They live in groups ranging from one to hundreds in the ocean. Bottlenose dolphins have teeth and eat fish, squid, krill and other crustaceans.

1. Which of the whales described above are Baleen Whales? _____

2. What is the difference between Baleen Whales and Toothed Whales?_____

3. How fast can a Killer Whale swim? _____

4. Which of the above whales is on the endangered species list? _____

5. Which whale has a hump in front of its fin?_____

Graphic Development

Directions: Read the following information and use the map below to answer the questions.

Keiko the whale is probably the most popular whale ever known, but he has paid a price for his popularity. Keiko has lived most of his life in captivity. Keiko was captured in the Atlantic Ocean near Iceland. He was taken to an aquarium in Iceland. From there he was moved to Canada, Mexico, Oregon, and his final destination will soon be back in Iceland. Keiko has spent most of his time in and around the oceans of the North American continent.

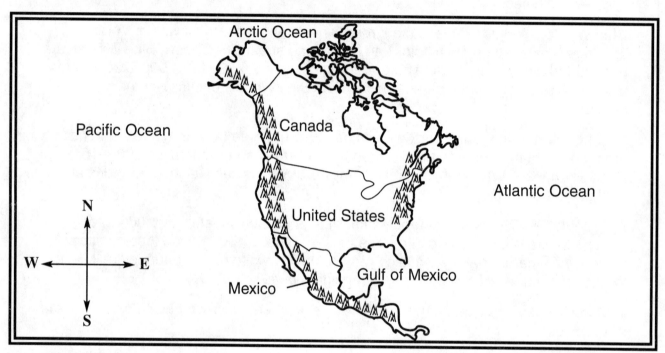

1. Most of the mountains are in what part of the North American continent?

   _____

2. What is the name of the ocean where Keiko was captured? Is it east or west of North America?

   _____

3. Newport, Oregon, is on the northwest corner of the United States. What ocean is near there?

   _____

4. Keiko spent some of his time in Mexico. Is Mexico north or south of the U.S.?

   _____

5. What ocean is at the northernmost part of the North American continent?

   _____

Answer Key

Lesson 1

Page 19
Sentence Comprehension
1. F
2. F
3. F
4. T
5. T

Word Study
1. all-purpose
2. X-ray
3. dot-matix
4. T-bone
5. PG-rated
6. Fourteen-year-old

Page 20
Paragraph Comprehension
1. a
2. c
3. d
4. b
5. b

Page 22
Whole Story Comprehension
1. b
2. c
3. c
4. c
5. a
6. a
7. d
8. a

Page 23
Enrichment
1. G
2. B
3. C
4. E
5. D
6. A
7. F

Page 24
Graphic Development
1. arm control
2. Reading
3. Face Control
4. Sight
5. Speech
6. Hearing
7. Leg Control

Lesson 2

Page 25
Sentence Comprehension
1. F
2. F
3. T
4. F
5. F

Word Study
Answers will vary.

Page 26
Paragraph Comprehension
1. b
2. c
3. d
4. d
5. c

Page 28
Whole Story Comprehension
1. b
2. a
3. b
4. b
5. a
6. b
7. b
8. d

Page 29
Enrichment
1. tone /setting
2. cause/effect
3. series
4. association
5. synonyms

Page 30
Graphic Development
1. Author hears noise.
2. author, cat
3. heard noise
4. The author saw the cat grin.
5. Author removes utensils, then cat.

Lesson 3

Page 31
Sentence Comprehension
1. T
2. T
3. F
4. T
5. F

Word Study
1. thump, thump 2. crunch 3. fizz
4. sssss 5. tick-tock 6. bang

Page 32
Paragraph Comprehension
1. c
2. c
3. a
4. d
5. b

Page 34
Whole Story Comprehension
1. a
2. b
3. d
4. a
5. c
6. b
7. d
8. d

Page 35
Enrichment
1. legs like rubber
2. walk like chickens
3. hands like pieces of wood
4. fast as a steam locomotive

Page 36
Graphic Development
1. 3,000
2. male runners
3. 2,000
4. More male runners in 1997
5. 9,000

Lesson 4

Page 37
Sentence Comprehension
1. F
2. T
3. T
4. T
5. F

Word Study
1. rodeo
2. commode
3. lariat
4. mustang
5. croissants

Page 38
Paragraph Comprehension
1. c
2. b
3. a
4. d
5. c

Page 40
Whole Story Comprehension
1. c
2. c
3. b
4. a
5. a
6. c
7. b
8. c

Page 41
Enrichment
1. I hope that I can get tickets to *Phantom of the Opera.*
2. The name of the movie showing right now is *Return of the Jedi.*
3. My favorite song right now is "Out of My Dreams..."
4. *Better Homes and Gardens* has...
5. Where did you put today's issue of the *Chicago Tribune*?

Page 42
Graphic Development
1. *Girls Got It*
2. 50,000
3. *Girls Got* It Book Sales
4. It will keep dropping.
5. 20,000

Lesson 5

Page 43
Sentence Comprehension
1. F
2. T
3. T
4. F
5. T

Answer Key (cont.)

Word Study
1. mischief
2. tomorrow
3. embarrassed
4. making
5. mysteries
6. answers

Page 44

Paragraph Comprehension
1. b
2. c
3. d
4. a
5. a

Page 46

Whole Story Comprehension
1. d
2. b
3. c
4. a
5. a
6. c
7. a
8. c

Page 47

Enrichment
1. "I thought they were an amazing pair," said Jane.
2. "Lewis and Clark were anything but litterbugs," stated the teacher.
3. "Where did L&C start their journey?" asked Fred.
4. "L&C began in Louisiana?" questioned Sandy.
5. Mr. Roy asked, "But where did they stop?"

Page 48

Graphic Development
1. Lewis & Clark Expedition
2. St. Louis
3. Northwest
4. 15
5. Ft. Mandan, Great Falls, Fort Clatsop

Lesson 6

Page 49

Sentence Comprehension
1. T
2. F
3. T
4. T
5. F

Word Study
1. 90,000,000
2. 64,000,000
3. 25,000,000
4. 90,000,000,000
5. 2,000,000,000,000

Page 50

Paragraph Comprehension
1. a
2. d
3. c
4. c
5. b

Page 52

Whole Story Comprehension
1. c
2. a
3. a
4. b
5. c
6. d
7. b
8. c

Page 53

Enrichment
1. G
2. F
3. E
4. H
5. B
6. D
7. A
8. I
9. C

Page 54

Graphic Development
1. Dating Dinosaurs
2. million years ago
3. Mesozoic Era
4. 2500 to 544 mya
5. Cenozoic Era

Lesson 7

Page 55

Sentence Comprehension
1. F
2. T
3. F
4. F
5. T

Word Study
1. newspaper – paper with news on it
2. cowboy – a male who works with cows
3. hairnet – a net used to cover the head
4. homebound – heading for home

Page 56

Paragraph Comprehension
1. d
2. c
3. d
4. b
5. a

Page 58

Whole Story Comprehension
1. d
2. a
3. b
4. c
5. d
6. a
7. c
8. b

Page 59

Enrichment
1. CD
2. megabytes
3. URL, Web site
4. LEGOS
5. DVD

Page 60

Graphic Development
1. Gulf of Santa Catalina
2. north
3. CA's smaller cities
4. south
5. I-5

Lesson 8

Page 61

Sentence Comprehension
1. F
2. T
3. T
4. T
5. F

Word Study
1. g
2. d
3. b
4. e
5. h
6. a

Page 62

Paragraph Comprehension
1. c
2. b
3. c
4. a
5. b

Page 64

Whole Story Comprehension
1. b
2. d
3. b
4. b
5. a
6. d
7. c
8. a

Page 65

Enrichment
1, 3, 5

Page 66

Graphic Development
1. Parking Zone
2. No Cars
3. Both directions of traffic
4. Stop sign
5. Right turn

Lesson 9

Page 67

Sentence Comprehension
1. T
2. F
3. F
4. T
5. F

Answer Key (cont.)

Word Study
1. Sandy
2. November
3. Grandma
4. Nan
5. Thanksgiving
6. Heidi

Page 68

Paragraph Comprehension
1. c
2. b
3. a
4. d
5. d

Page 70

Whole Story Comprehension
1. d
2. a
3. b
4. b
5. c
6. b
7. c
8. b

Page 71

Enrichment
1. positive/negative
2. positive/negative
3. negative/positive
4. negative/positive
5. positive/negative
6. positive/negative

Page 72

Graphic Development
1. Number of boys & girls playing video games from 1995-1999
2. 50 million
3. Video Game Mania
4. 15 million
5. 25 million

Lesson 10

Page 73

Sentence Comprehension
1. T
2. F
3. T
4. F
5. T

Word Study
1. amazing
2. curious
3. nutritious
4. together
5. mothering
6. sandwiches

Page 74

Paragraph Comprehension
1. d
2. a
3. b
4. b
5. c

Page 76

Whole Story Comprehension
1. d
2. c
3. a
4. a
5. c
6. b
7. a
8. d

Page 77

Enrichment
1. even
2. Because
3. Although
4. now
5. And finally

Page 78

Graphic Development
1. milk allergy
2. five more people
3. Kids with Allergies at Hualapai Elementary School
4. Pollen allergy
5. 35 people

Lesson 11

Page 79

Sentence Comprehension
1. F
2. T
3. F
4. F
5. F

Word Study
1. state of moving together
2. state of sending
3. person who places music together
4. action of moving out feelings
5. to place out
6. the condition of sounding out again

Page 80

Paragraph Comprehension
1. c
2. c
3. a
4. d
5. b

Page 82

Whole Story Comprehension
1. a
2. c
3. b
4. d
5. a
6. b
7. d
8. d

Page 83

Enrichment
Answers will vary.

Page 84

Graphic Development
1. straighten rivers and build canals
2. 1980s
3. Trouble in the Everglades
4. Large numbers of people began settling in Florida.
5. phosphorus

Lesson 12

Page 85

Sentence Comprehension
1. T
2. T
3. T
4. F
5. F

Word Study
1. join, unite, combine
2. question, inquire
3. naughty, evil, wicked
4. under, below
5. valiant, brave, daring
6. bright, radiant
7. summon, command
8. make, construct
9. bring, lug, transport
10. youngsters, kids

Page 86

Paragraph Comprehension
1. b
2. c
3. a
4. b
5. d

Page 88

Whole Story Comprehension
1. b
2. d
3. d
4. c
5. d
6. c
7. b
8. c

Page 89

Enrichment
1. sales
2. suspects
3. addresses
4. Beanies
5. beans
6. potatoes
7. leaves
8. deer
9. worries
10. bunches
11. teeth
12. collectors
13. messes
14. companies
15. inches
16. coaches
17. beliefs
18. thieves

Answer Key *(cont.)*

Page 90

Graphic Development

1. 1998
2. Teddy
3. *Mary Beth's Bean Bag World*
4. The Rise and Fall of Beanies
5. $1,000

Lesson 13

Page 91

Sentence Comprehension

1. T
2. F
3. F
4. T
5. F

Word Study

1. natural
2. weakness/weaken
3. friendship
4. carelessness
5. agreeable

Page 92

Paragraph Comprehension

1. c
2. d
3. d
4. a
5. b

Page 94

Whole Story Comprehension

1. b
2. a
3. d
4. c
5. c
6. b
7. b
8. c

Page 95

Enrichment

5,1,4,2,3

Page 96

Graphic Development

1. 1 student
2. 8 people
3. Tea Cups
4. 25 people
5. none

Lesson 14

Page 97

Sentence Comprehension

1. T
2. F
3. F
4. T
5. T

Word Study

1. sparkle
2. spat
3. speak
4. spark
5. sparrow

Page 98

Paragraph Comprehension

1. b
2. d
3. c
4. a
5. b

Page 100

Whole Story Comprehension

1. b
2. d
3. b
4. c
5. c
6. a
7. c
8. b

Page 101

Enrichment

1, 4, 5, 7, 8

Page 102

Graphic Development

1. 3
2. national park sites
3. The Wrong Move?
4. Botswana, Namibia, Zimbabwe
5. Hluhluwe-Umfolozi

Lesson 15

Page 103

Sentence Comprehension

1. T
2. F
3. T
4. T
5. F

Word Study

1. FBI
2. DARE
3. CIA
4. IBM
5. IRS
6. NASA

Page 104

Paragraph Comprehension

1. b
2. d
3. a
4. c
5. c

Page 106

Whole Story Comprehension

1. c
2. b
3. c
4. c
5. a
6. c
7. b
8. d

Page 107

Enrichment

1. the community itself
2. teaches an alternative to violence and delinquency
3. self-esteem
4. Youth Enrichment Services

Page 108

Graphic Development

1. touring dairy farms, camping, doing service projects
2. service projects
3. Super Summer Activities
4. touring dairy farms
5. camping

Lesson 16

Page 109

Sentence Comprehension

1. T
2. F
3. T
4. F
5. F

Word Study

1. found
2. opened
3. looked
4. succeeded
5. completed
6. waited
7. chained
8. wanted

Page 110

Paragraph Comprehension

1. c
2. b
3. a
4. b
5. d

Page 112

Whole Story Comprehension

1. b
2. c
3. d
4. c
5. a
6. a
7. d
8. b

Page 113

Enrichment

1. fish or other squid, sometimes whales
2. males get about 25 feet, females about 60 feet
3. the largest invertebrate
4. It rips chunks of flesh from the prey with its beak.
5. causes the squid to rise

Page 114

Graphic Development

1. blue whale
2. 30 feet
3. Large Animals of the Sea
4. 25 feet
5. 40 feet

Answer Key (cont.)

Lesson 17

Page 115
Sentence Comprehension
1. F
2. F
3. F
4. T
5. T

Word Study
1. hot
2. wet
3. hard
4. heavy, dark
5. weak
6. night
7. long
8. afraid
9. bad
10. over
11. up
12. in

Page 116
Paragraph Comprehension
1. d
2. b
3. c
4. a
5. b

Page 118
Whole Story Comprehension
1. b
2. a
3. c
4. d
5. b
6. a
7. c
8. d

Page 119
Enrichment
1. yes
2. yes
3. proper nouns, proper adjectives
4. first words in quotation

Page 120
Graphic Development
1. the similarities and differences between *Star Wars* and *Phantom Menace*
2. Both movies are based on fictional people/places and both required computer artists.
3. Phantom Menace
4. computer artists
5. both

Lesson 18

Page 121
Sentence Comprehension
1. F
2. T
3. F
4. F
5. T

Word Study
1. enormous
2. small
3. fun
4. new
5. cute
6. wicked

Page 122
Paragraph Comprehension
1. b
2. c
3. b
4. c
5. d

Page 124
Whole Story Comprehension
1. a
2. c
3. d
4. b
5. b
6. a
7. c
8. a

Page 125
Enrichment
2. graduation or graduate
3. champion
4. bicycle
5. veterinarian
6. trigonometry
7. automobile
8. mathematics
9. telephone
10. convict

Page 126
Graphic Development
1. "Night in Terror Tower"
2. 21 students
3. three
4. two
5. no

Lesson 19

Page 127
Sentence Comprehension
1. F
2. T
3. F
4. F
5. T

Word Study
1. hyper
2. inter
3. cir
4. cata
5. co
6. semi
7. hexa
8. intro
9. inter
10. extra

Page 128
Paragraph Comprehension
1. b
2. a
3. c
4. d
5. b

Page 130
Whole Story Comprehension
1. d
2. c
3. a
4. c
5. c
6. b
7. c
8. d

Page 131
Enrichment
1. series of words
2. to set off dialogue
3. between two clauses

Page 132
Graphic Development
1. Characters from Harry *Potter and the Sorcerer's Stone*
2. Albus Dumbledore
3. 3
4. On Harry's side, twice as tall as men
5. Harry Potter

Lesson 20

Page 133
Sentence Comprehension
1. T
2. T
3. F
4. F
5. F

Word Study
1. inches
2. miles
3. centimeters
4. yards
5. feet
6. decimeters

Page 134
Paragraph Comprehension
1. a
2. c
3. b
4. b
5. c

Page 136
Whole Story Comprehension
1. c
2. b
3. b
4. c
5. d
6. a
7. a
8. b

Page 137
Enrichment
1. Blue, Humpback, and Minke Whales
2. Baleen Whales don't have teeth.
3. 34 mph
4. Blue Whale
5. Humpback Whale

Page 138
Graphic Development
1. Western side
2. North Atlantic Ocean, east
3. Pacific Ocean
4. south
5. Arctic

Answer Sheet

Directions: Fill in the bubble of the correct answer "a," "b," "c," "d," or "e" on this sheet. If the answer is "True," fill in the "a" bubble, and if the answer is "False," fill in the "b" bubble.

T F   T F   T F   T F